S0-BII-045

PRENTICE HALL

SCIENCE EXPLORER

Grade 7

Guided Reading and Study Workbook

Student Edition

Prentice Hall

Needham, Massachusetts
Upper Saddle River, New Jersey
Glenview, Illinois

Copyright © 2002 by Prentice-Hall, Inc., Upper Saddle River, New Jersey 07458. All rights reserved. Printed in the United States of America. This publication is protected by copyright, and permission should be obtained from the publisher prior to any prohibited reproduction, storage in a retrieval system, or transmission in any form or by any means, electronic, mechanical, photocopying, recording, or likewise. Student worksheets and tests may be duplicated for classroom use, the number not to exceed the number of students in each class. Notice of copyright must appear on all copies. For information regarding permissions(s), write to: Rights and Permissions Department.

ISBN 0-13-058707-9
13 14 15 16 17   08 07 06

Table of Contents

© Prentice-Hall, Inc.

TABLE OF CONTENTS *(continued)*

© Prentice-Hall, Inc.

WHAT IS SCIENCE?
(pages 10-19)

This section explains the skills that scientists use to solve problems and find answers. It also tells about safety in the laboratory and branches of science.

▶ **Introduction** (page 10)

1. A way of learning about the natural world is _____.

2. What is scientific inquiry? _____

_____

▶ **Thinking Like a Scientist** (pages 10–15)

3. Circle the letter of the skill that scientific inquiry usually begins with.

   a. designing an experiment   **b.** asking a question

   c. collecting data   **d.** communicating

4. Is the following sentence true or false? An inference is a fact.

   _____

5. Is the following sentence true or false? A hypothesis is a possible

   explanation for a set of observations. _____

6. What is a controlled experiment? _____

_____

7. Circle the letter of the manipulated variable in the tomato plant
   experiment.

   a. sunlight   **b.** water   **c.** height   **d.** fertilizer

8. The facts, figures, and other observations that are gathered through

   using one or more of your senses are called _____.

© Prentice-Hall, Inc.

What Is Science? *(continued)*

9. Why is it important for scientists to use a standard system of

measurement? _____

_____

_____

10. Use this graph to answer the questions below.

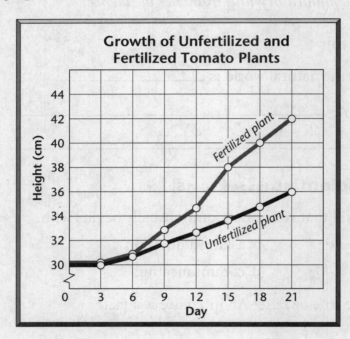

Growth of Unfertilized and Fertilized Tomato Plants

a. Compare the heights of the two tomato plants after six days.

_____

b. Compare the heights of the two tomato plants after 21 days.

_____

11. What does it mean to draw a conclusion? _____

_____

12. How do scientists communicate their conclusions to other scientists?

_____

_____

© Prentice-Hall, Inc.

▶ **Scientific Theories and Laws** (page 16)

13. What is a scientific theory? _____

_____

14. Is the following sentence true of false? Future testing can prove a

scientific theory to be incorrect. _____

▶ **Laboratory Safety** (page 16)

15. Circle the letter of each safe laboratory practice.

   a. Show respect to your teacher and classmates.

   b. Wear proper safety equipment.

   c. Handle lab materials carefully.

   d. Keep your work area neat and clean.

▶ **Branches of Science** (pages 18–19)

16. List the four main branches of science.

   a. _____   **b.** _____

   c. _____   **d.** _____

▶ **Technology and the Internet** (page 19)

17. Circle the letter of each way that scientists use technology.

   a. Microscopes to see tiny viruses

   b. Telescopes to make models

   c. Computers to make graphs

   d. Internet to communicate

 Reading Skill Practice

A concept map is a useful tool to organize information. Make a concept map to show the skills that scientists use in an investigation. For more information about concept maps, see page 660 in the Skills Handbook of your textbook.

© Prentice-Hall, Inc.

What Is Science? *(continued)*

WordWise

Answer the questions by writing the correct key term in the blanks. Use the circled letter in each term to find the hidden key term. Then write a definition for the hidden key term.

What is a factor that can be changed in an experiment?

_ _ _ Ⓞ _ _ _ _

What includes all of the knowledge gained while exploring the natural world?

_ _ _ _ Ⓞ _ _

What is a well-tested concept that explains a wide range of observations?

_ _ _ _ _ _ _ Ⓞ _ _   _ _ _ _ _ _

What is a possible explanation for a set of observations?

_ _ _ _ _ _ Ⓞ _ _ _

What skill involves using one or more of your senses to gather information and collect data?

_ _ _ _ Ⓞ _ _ _ _ _

What is the factor that changes in an experiment because of the manipulated variable?

_ Ⓞ _ _ _ _ _ _ _ _   _ _ _ _ _ _ _

What is the one variable that is changed in an experiment to test a hypothesis?

_ _ Ⓞ _ _ _ _ _ _ _ _   _ _ _ _ _ _ _ _

What is an experiment in which all of the variables except for one remain the same?

Ⓞ _ _ _ _ _ _ _ _ _   _ _ _ _ _ _ _ _ _ _

What term describes the many ways in which scientists study the natural world?

_ _ _ Ⓞ _ _ _ _ _   _ _ _ _ _ _ _

Key Term: _ _ _ _ _ _ _ _ _

Definition: _____

_____

© Prentice-Hall, Inc.

CHAPTER 1

THE PROPERTIES OF MATTER

© Prentice-Hall, Inc.

SECTION 1-1 **Matter and Changes in Matter**
(pages 24-30)

This section describes properties of matter and how matter can be classified. The section also describes ways in which matter can change.

▶ Physical and Chemical Properties of Matter (page 25)

1. Is the following sentence true or false? Physical and chemical properties of matter are characteristics used to classify and describe a particular

   substance. _____

2. What is a physical property? _____

   _____

   _____

3. What is a chemical property? _____

   _____

▶ Elements, Compounds, and Mixtures (pages 26–27)

4. Complete the following table.

Matter	
Kind of Matter	**Definition**
	Substance that cannot be broken down into other substances by chemical or physical means
Compound	
	Two or more substances in the same place that are not chemically combined

CHAPTER 1, The Properties of Matter (continued)

5. Oxygen, tin, and argon are examples of _____.

6. Table salt and water are examples of _____.

7. The ratio of elements in a compound is shown by the compound's

_____.

8. Is the following sentence true or false? The properties of a compound

are very similar to its elements. _____

9. Is the following sentence true or false? The substances in a mixture

keep their original properties. _____

▶ Changes in Matter (pages 27–29)

10. Complete the concept map.

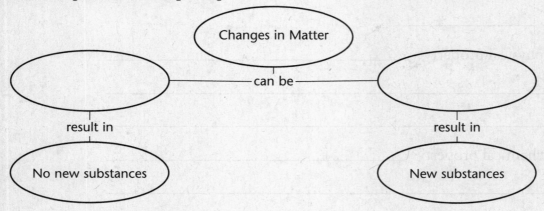

11. Complete the table to classify changes as chemical or physical.

Changes	
Kind of Change	**Example**
	Melting of ice
	Burning of wood
	Rusting of metal
	Breaking of boulders
	Tarnishing of metal

© Prentice-Hall, Inc.

▶ Reading Chemical Equations (page 28)

12. What is a chemical equation? _____

_____

_____

13. Write this equation in words: $C + O_2 \longrightarrow CO_2$ _____

_____

14. The substances you start with in a chemical reaction are called the

_____ .

15. The substances that are present at the end of a chemical reaction are

called the _____ .

▶ Chemical Reactions on a Small Scale (page 30)

16. Complete the concept map.

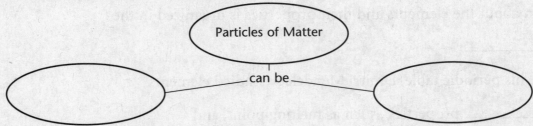

17. The smallest particle of an element is a(n) _____ .

18. What is a molecule? _____

_____

19. Circle the letter of each sentence that is true of chemical bonds.

    a. They can be formed during a chemical reaction.

    b. They are found within atoms.

    c. They can be broken during a chemical reaction.

    d. They hold atoms together.

© Prentice-Hall, Inc.

CHAPTER 1, The Properties of Matter *(continued)*

 Reading Skill Practice

Knowing the meanings of key terms in a section will help you to better understand what you are reading. Make a list of key terms in this section. Write the meanings of these terms using your own words. In this way, the key terms become a natural part of your vocabulary. Do your work on a separate sheet of paper.

SECTION 1-2 **Organizing the Elements**
(pages 31-37)

This section explains how chemical and physical properties of elements can be used to organize and classify elements.

▶ **Organizing Elements by Their Properties** (page 32)

1. Information about the elements and their properties is organized in the

   _____.

2. To organize his periodic table, Dmitri Mendeleev studied elements'

   _____ properties , such as melting point, and

   _____ properties, such as the types of compounds they
   form.

3. The average mass of one atom of an element is called the

   _____ of that element.

4. Circle the letter of each statement that is true of Mendeleev's periodic table.

   a. Mendeleev arranged elements according to the diameters of their atoms.

   b. Mendeleev left spaces where he expected unknown elements belonged.

   c. Mendeleev found that there were groups of elements with similar
   properties.

   d. Mendeleev's predictions of new elements were incorrect.

© Prentice-Hall, Inc.

▶ Today's Periodic Table (pages 33–35)

5. List the three particles that make up atoms.

   a. _____ b. _____ c. _____

6. What is an element's atomic number? _____

   _____

7. The modern periodic table is organized by _____ atomic numbers of the elements.

8. Elements in the same column of the periodic table are called a

   _____, or family.

9. A row across the periodic table is called a(n) _____.

10. Label the symbol, atomic number, and atomic mass in this square from the periodic table.

▶ Identifying Patterns and Properties (pages 36–37)

11. Is the following sentence true or false? You can predict some of an element's physical properties, but none of its chemical properties, based

    on the element's location in the periodic table. _____

12. Complete the concept map.

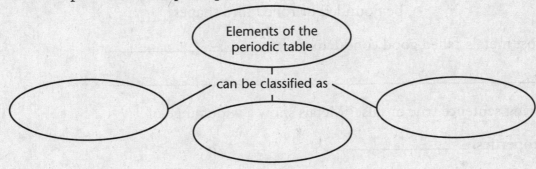

© Prentice-Hall, Inc.

CHAPTER 1, The Properties of Matter *(continued)*

Metals
(pages 39-44)

This section describes the properties of metals and the characteristics of the different groups, or families, of metals.

▶ What Is a Metal? (pages 39–40)

1. Chemists classify an element as a metal based on what physical properties?

   a. _____   b. _____

   c. _____   d. _____

2. Is the following sentence true or false? Most metals are solids at room temperatures because they have very low melting points.

   _____

Match the term with its definition.

	Term	Definition
_____	3. malleable	a. The process of reaction and wearing away of a metal element
_____	4. ductile	b. A characteristic of those metals that are attracted to magnets or can be made into magnets
_____	5. magnetic	c. A term used to describe a material that can be pulled out, or drawn, into a long wire
_____	6. corrosion	d. A term used to describe a material that can be pounded or rolled into shapes

7. Why are most metals called good conductors? _____

   _____

8. Is the following sentence true or false? Metals show a wide range of

   chemical properties. _____

© Prentice-Hall, Inc.

▶ Alloys (page 41)

9. A mixture of two or more elements that has the properties of a metal is called a(n) _____.

10. Bronze is a mixture of what two metals? _____

▶ Metals in the Periodic Table (pages 41–44)

11. How do the properties of each family of metals change as you move

    across the table? _____

    _____

12. Circle the letter of each sentence that is true about alkali metals.

    a. They are never found as elements but only in compounds.

    b. As elements, they are soft and shiny.

    c. They are often found as pure elements in sea water.

    d. They are extremely reactive.

13. What are the two most important alkali metals?

    _____

14. Circle the letter of each sentence that is true about alkaline earth metals.

    a. They are good conductors of electricity.

    b. They are never found uncombined in nature.

    c. They are bright white and fairly hard.

    d. They are much less reactive than most metals.

15. What are the two most common alkaline earth metals?

    _____

16. Circle the letter of each element that is a transition metal.

    a. gold   **b.** iron   **c.** copper   **d.** lithium

17. Is the following sentence true or false? The transition metals are fairly

    stable, reacting slowly or not at all with air and water. _____

© Prentice-Hall, Inc.

CHAPTER 1, The Properties of Matter *(continued)*

18. Lanthanides and actinides are found in periods 6 and 7 within the

_____.

19. Where are the lanthanides and actinides placed on the periodic table?

_____

20. Uranium has an atomic number of 92. How were all the elements with

atomic numbers higher than 92 created? _____

_____

21. Complete the concept map about metals.

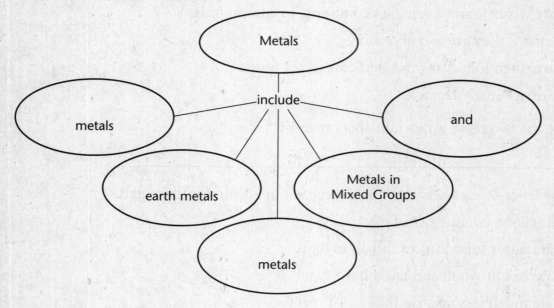

© Prentice-Hall, Inc.

SECTION 1–4 Nonmetals and Metalloids (pages 48-54)

This section describes properties of the elements on the periodic table that are not metals.

▶ What Is a Nonmetal? (pages 48–49)

1. The elements that lack most of the properties of metals are called

_____.

Science Explorer *Grade 7*

2. Where are the nonmetals found on the periodic table? _____

_____

_____

3. Is the following sentence true or false? Many of the nonmetals are gases

at room temperature. _____

4. Circle the letter of each sentence that is true about the physical
properties of nonmetals.

   a. Solid nonmetals are brittle.

   b. They usually have lower densities than metals.

   c. Most are shiny.

   d. They are good conductors of both heat and electricity.

5. Except for the Group 18 elements, most nonmetals readily form

_____.

6. What happens when nonmetals and metals react? _____

_____

_____

7. A molecule composed of two atoms is called a(n)

_____.

▶ **Families of Nonmetals** (pages 50–53)

   8. Group 14 is also known as the _____ family.

   9. The only nonmetal in Group 14 is _____.

10. All living things contain what kind of compounds? _____

_____

_____

11. What are the nonmetals in Group 15? _____

12. Air is almost 80 percent _____.

© Prentice-Hall, Inc.

CHAPTER 1, The Properties of Matter *(continued)*

13. Circle the letter of each sentence that is true about oxygen.

   a. The oxygen you breathe is a diatomic molecule.

   b. Oxygen rarely combines with other elements.

   c. Oxygen is the most abundant element in Earth's crust.

   d. Ozone collects in a layer in the upper atmosphere.

14. Is the following sentence true or false? Most halogens are dangerous to

   humans. _____

15. Circle the letter of each sentence that is true about the noble gases.

   a. They exist in large amounts in the atmosphere.

   b. They are chemically very stable and unreactive.

   c. They were discovered in the early 1700s

   d. They are used in glowing electric lights.

16. Complete the table about families of nonmetals.

Nonmetals		
Family	**Group**	**Nonmetals in Family**
Carbon family		
Nitrogen family		
Oxygen family		
Halogen family		
Noble gases		

© Prentice-Hall, Inc.

17. Where on the periodic table is hydrogen found? _____

_____

18. How many protons and electrons does a hydrogen atom usually contain?

_____

_____

19. Why can't hydrogen be grouped in a family? _____

_____

_____

20. Is the following question true or false? Most of the hydrogen found on

Earth is combined with oxygen in water. _____

▶ The Metalloids (page 54)

21. What are metalloids? _____

_____

22. How many metalloids are shown in the periodic table?

_____

23. What is the most common metalloid? _____

24. What is the most useful property of the metalloids? _____

_____

_____

25. What are semiconductors? _____

_____

_____

26. Where are semiconductors used? _____

_____

© Prentice-Hall, Inc.

CHAPTER 1, The Properties of Matter (continued)

WordWise

Use the clues to help you unscramble the key terms from Chapter 1. Then put the numbered letters in order to find the answer to the riddle.

Clues	Key Terms

Clues   **Key Terms**

A substance made of two or more elements   doncumop   _ _ _ _ _ _ _ _
that are chemically combined in a set ratio   1

A term used to describe a material   llbeealam _ _ _ _ _ _ _ _ _
that can be pounded or rolled into shape   2

The gradual wearing away   rsoooincr _ _ _ _ _ _ _ _
of a metal element   3   4

A particle outside the nucleus of an atom   nocleetr   _ _ _ _ _ _ _ _
                                                                 5

A horizontal row across the periodic table   roiedp   _ _ _ _ _ _
                                                                      6

An element that has some   ldmtioael _ _ _ _ _ _ _ _ _
characteristics of a metal and   7
some characteristics of a nonmetal

A term used to describe a material that   lecuitd   _ _ _ _ _ _ _
can be drawn into a long wire   8 9

The number of protons   mtoica meunrb   _ _ _ _ _ _   _ _ _ _ _ _
in the nucleus of an atom   10

The elements in Group 18 of   beoln ssgea   _ _ _ _ _   _ _ _ _ _
the periodic table   11

Elements in the first row of   sletahnaidn   _ _ _ _ _ _ _ _ _ _ _
the rare earth elements of the   12   13
periodic table

Riddle: What chart shows the repeating properties of elements?

Answer: _ _ _ _ _ _ _ _   _ _ _ _ _
             1 2 3 4 5 6 7 8   9 10 11 12 13

© Prentice-Hall, Inc.

CHAPTER 2

ELEMENTS FORMING COMPOUNDS

....

SECTION 2-1 **Atoms and Ionic Bonds** (pages 60-67)

This section describes the structure of an atom and explains how an atom becomes electrically charged. It also describes how bonds are formed between charged atoms.

▶ Inside an Atom (pages 60–61)

1. Electrons that are farther away from the nucleus or most loosely held by

   the nucleus are called _____.

2. The symbol of an element surrounded by dots is called a(n)

   _____.

▶ Valence Electrons and the Periodic Table (page 62)

3. Is the following sentence true or false? All atoms in the same period have

   the same number of valence electrons. _____

4. A neutral atom never has more than _____ valence

   electrons.

▶ Electron Transfer and Bonding (pages 62–63)

5. An atom or group of atoms that has become electrically charged is a(n)

   _____.

6. What happens to an atom when it loses an electron? _____

   _____

7. What happens to an atom when it gains an electron? _____

   _____

© Prentice-Hall, Inc.

CHAPTER 2, Elements Forming Compounds *(continued)*

▶ Forming an Ionic Bond (pages 63–64)

8. What is an ionic bond? _____

_____

9. What kind of ions do a sodium atom and a chlorine atom become

when a valence electron is transferred from one to the other? _____

_____

_____

10. Use Figure 5 on page 63 to complete the table.

Ions and Their Charges		
Name	**Charge**	**Symbol or Formula**
Sodium		
Magnesium		
Chloride		
Sulfate		

11. What does the formula for the compound magnesium chloride, $MgCl_2$,
tell you about how many chloride ions are needed to cancel out the

charge of a magnesium ion? _____

_____

▶ Polyatomic Ions (page 65)

12. Ions that are made of more than one atom are called

_____.

13. How many atoms make up the carbonate ion (CO_3^{2-}), and what is its

charge? _____

_____

© Prentice-Hall, Inc.

▶ Naming Ionic Compounds (page 65)

14. Is the following sentence true or false? In an ionic compound, the name

of the negative ion comes first. _____

15. When does the end of a name of a negative ion become *-ide*? _____

_____

▶ Physical Properties of Ionic Compounds (pages 66–67)

16. What are three characteristic properties of ionic compounds?

a. _____

b. _____

c. _____

17. An orderly, three-dimensional arrangement formed by ions is called

a(n) _____.

18. In an ionic compound, every ion is attracted to what other ions? _____

_____

_____

19. At room temperature, ionic bonds are strong enough to cause all ionic

compounds to be _____.

20. When do ionic compounds conduct electricity well? _____

_____

 Reading Skill Practice

A flowchart can help you remember the order in which events occur. On a separate sheet of paper, create a flowchart that describes the steps that take place when sodium and chlorine atoms form an ionic bond. This process is explained in *Exploring Ionic Bonds* on page 64. For more information about flowcharts, see page 661 in the Skills Handbook of your textbook.

© Prentice-Hall, Inc.

CHAPTER 2, Elements Forming Compounds *(continued)*

• •

SECTION 2-2 Atoms and Covalent Bonds (pages 69-73)

This section describes how a chemical bond forms when two atoms share electrons. It also describes how electrons are shared unequally in some chemical bonds.

▶ **Electron Sharing** (page 69)

1. What is a covalent bond? _____

_____

2. On the dot diagram below, draw a circle around the shared electrons that form a covalent bond between two fluorine atoms.

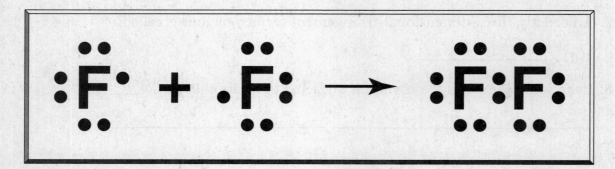

3. Circle the letter of the sentence that is true about a covalent bond in a molecule of fluorine.

   a. Only the right atom attracts the two electrons in the middle.

   b. Both atoms lose electrons.

   c. Both atoms attract the two shared electrons at the same time.

   d. Only the left atom attracts the two electrons in the middle.

▶ **How Many Bonds?** (page 70)

4. In the dot diagram of an oxygen molecule in Figure 10 on page 70, how many covalent bonds are in the molecule? _____

5. A chemical bond formed when atoms share two pairs of electrons is

   called a(n) _____.

© Prentice-Hall, Inc.

▶ Physical Properties of Molecular Compounds (pages 70–71)

6. What do molecular compounds consist of? _____

_____

_____

7. Circle the letter of each sentence that is true about molecular compounds.

  a. More heat is needed to separate molecules from one another than is needed to separate ions.

  b. They melt at much lower temperatures than do ionic compounds.

  c. They boil at much lower temperatures than do ionic compounds.

  d. They are poor conductors of electricity.

▶ Unequal Sharing of Electrons (pages 71–72)

8. How do molecules come to have a slight electrical charge?

_____

_____

_____

_____

9. In a polar covalent bond, electrons are shared _____.

10. How are electrons shared in a nonpolar covalent bond? _____

_____

_____

11. How can a molecule be nonpolar even when it has polar bonds? _____

_____

_____

12. Is the following sentence true or false? Water molecules are polar.

_____

© Prentice-Hall, Inc.

CHAPTER 2, Elements Forming Compounds *(continued)*

▶ Attractions Between Molecules (pages 72–73)

13. Why do polar and nonpolar molecules have different properties? _____

_____

_____

14. Why don't water and vegetable oil mix? _____

_____

_____

_____

15. When you do laundry, what causes nonpolar dirt to mix with the

polar water? _____

_____

_____

· ·

SECTION 2-3 **Crystal Chemistry**
(pages 76-78)

This section explains how chemical bonds are related to the properties of minerals.

▶ The Physical Properties of Minerals (pages 76–77)

1. A naturally occurring solid that has a crystal structure and a definite

chemical composition is called a(n) _____.

2. What properties do mineralogists use to identify minerals? _____

_____

_____

3. What do all the properties of a mineral depend on? _____

_____

© Prentice-Hall, Inc.

▶ Bonding in Mineral Crystals (pages 77–78)

4. Is the following sentence true or false? All mineral crystals are made of

ions. _____

5. What determines mineral properties such as crystal shape, hardness,

and the way the crystal breaks apart? _____

_____

_____

6. Complete the table about mineral crystals.

Characteristics of Two Minerals		
Mineral	**How It Breaks**	**Type of Crystal**
	Splits along face of like charges	
	Breaks apart into irregular shapes	

▶ Comparing Crystals (page 78)

7. Is the following sentence true or false? The stronger bonds of quartz

make it harder than halite. _____

8. If a mineralogist is in doubt about the identity of a mineral, what can he

or she do? _____

_____

_____

© Prentice-Hall, Inc.

CHAPTER 2, Elements Forming Compounds *(continued)*

WordWise

Answer the questions by writing the correct key terms in the blanks. Use the numbered letters in the terms to find the hidden key term. Then write a definition for the hidden key term.

Clues   **Key Terms**

_____ ions are made of more   — — — — — — — — — — —
than one atom.   1

What is a covalent bond called in which   — — — — —
electrons are shared unequally?   2

Molecular _____ are made of   — — — — — — — — — —
molecules having covalently bonded   3
atoms.

What is a naturally occuring solid with   — — — — — — —
a crystal structure?   4

What is an orderly, three-dimensional   — — — — — — —
arrangement formed by ions called?   5

What is a chemical bond formed when   — — — — — — — —   — — — —
two atoms share electrons?   6

What is a bond in which   — — — — — — — —
electrons are shared equally?   7

What is an atom or group of atoms that   — — —
has become electrically charged?   8

What is a bond in which two pairs of   — — — — — —   — — — —
electrons are shared between atoms?   9

Key Term: — — — — —   — — — —
                         1   2   3   4   5   6   7   8   9

Definition: _____

© Prentice-Hall, Inc.

CHAPTER 3

EVERYDAY CHANGES IN SUBSTANCES

• •

SECTION 3–1 **Understanding Solutions**
(pages 84–91)

This section explains what happens to particles of substances in solution. It also describes properties of solutions, including how well a solute can dissolve in a solvent.

▶ Solutions and Suspensions (pages 84–85)

1. What is a suspension? _____

_____

_____

2. A well-mixed mixture is called a(n) _____.

3. Circle the letter of the mixture that is evenly mixed throughout.

   a. mixture   **b.** solution

   c. suspension   **d.** compound

4. Circle the letter of each method you could use to separate salt from water.

   a. filtering   **b.** boiling

   c. evaporation   **d.** settling

▶ Solvents and Solutes (pages 85–86)

5. Complete the table about solvents and solutes.

Parts of a Solution		
Part	**Definition**	**Which Part of Salt Water Solution?**
	The part of a solution present in the largest amount	
	A substance present in a solution in a smaller amount	

© Prentice-Hall, Inc.

CHAPTER 3, Everyday Changes in Substances *(continued)*

6. In a solution, the _____ is dissolved by the

_____.

7. Why is water called the "universal solvent"? _____

_____

_____

8. According to the table in Figure 3 on page 86, what is the solute and

what is the solvent in the solution called air? _____

_____

_____

▶ Particles in a Solution (pages 86–87)

9. What happens to the solute's particles whenever a solution forms?

_____

_____

10. Circle the letter of each sentence that is true about particles in a solution.

　a. When an ionic solid mixes with water, its ions repel water molecules.

　b. When a molecular solid mixes with water, the covalent bonds are not
　　broken.

　c. When an ionic solid mixes with water, water molecules surround
　　each ion.

　d. When a molecular solid mixes with water, the solute's individual
　　molecules break up.

11. How could you use electrical conductivity to distinguish between a salt

solution and a sugar solution? _____

_____

_____

_____

© Prentice-Hall, Inc.

▶ Concentration (page 87)

12. The amount of solute dissolved in a certain amount of solvent is the

_____ of a solution.

13. Complete the table about concentrations.

Concentrations	
Type of Solution	**Definition**
Dilute solution	
Concentrated solution	

▶ Solubility (page 88)

14. What is solubility? _____

_____

_____

15. Complete the table about solutions.

Solutions	
Type of Solution	**Definition**
	A solution that contains as much dissolved solute as possible
	A solution that does not hold as much of a solute as possible

▶ Changing Solubility (pages 88–89)

16. What are two factors that affect the solubility of a substance?

a. _____   b. _____

17. What can you do to make a saturated solution hold more solid solute?

_____

_____

© Prentice-Hall, Inc.

CHAPTER 3, Everyday Changes in Substances *(continued)*

18. Circle the letter of each sentence that is true about temperature and solubility.

   a. Most solids become more soluble as the temperature goes up.

   b. Most gases become less soluble as the temperature goes up.

   c. Sugar dissolves better in cold water than in hot water.

   d. Carbon dioxide dissolves better in cold water than in hot water.

19. Is the following sentence true or false? Ionic and polar compounds

   usually dissolve in polar solvents. _____

▶ **Effects of Solutes on Solutions** (pages 90–91)

20. Circle the letter of each sentence that is true about the effects of solutes on solutions.

   a. Solutes raise the boiling point of a solvent.

   b. The temperature must drop lower than 0°C for water to freeze when a solute is dissolved in the water.

   c. Solutes raise the freezing point of a solvent.

   d. Antifreeze causes water to boil at a lower temperature than water alone does.

. . . .

SECTION 3-2 **Describing Acids and Bases**
(pages 94-99)

This section describes properties of compounds called acids and bases.

▶ **Properties of Acids** (pages 94–97)

1. What three properties are characteristic of an acid?

   a. _____

   b. _____

   c. _____

© Prentice-Hall, Inc.

2. If you were a scientist, why wouldn't you use "sour taste" to identify a

compound as acidic? _____

_____

_____

3. Why are acids often identified as corrosive? _____

_____

4. Circle the letter of the kind of rock that is made of calcium carbonate.

    a. granite   **b.** sandstone   **c.** limestone   **d.** coal

5. What happens when a dilute solution of hydrochloric acid is poured on

a limestone rock? _____

6. A compound that changes color in the presence of an acid or a base is

called a(n) _____.

7. Why does lemon juice turn blue litmus paper red? _____

_____

8. Is the following sentence true or false? Many of the vitamins in the foods

you eat are acids. _____

9. Complete the table using information in Figure 12 on page 95 and in
Exploring Uses of Acids on page 97.

Common Acids		
Acid	**Formula**	**Use**
Hydrochloric acid		
Nitric acid		
Sulfuric acid		
Phosphoric acid		

© Prentice-Hall, Inc.

CHAPTER 3, Everyday Changes in Substances (continued)

▶ Properties of Bases (pages 98–99)

10. What three properties are characteristic of a base?

    a. _____

    b. _____

    c. _____

11. Why do your hands feel slippery when you rub soap on them under water?

    _____

12. Is the following sentence true or false? Even a strong base can't hurt you

    if you touch it. _____

13. Is the following sentence true or false? A safe way to identify a base is to

    feel it. _____

14. Remembering the letter *b* will help you remember that

    b_____ turn litmus paper b_____.

15. Potassium hydroxide (KOH) and magnesium hydroxide ($Mg(OH)_2$) are

    examples of _____

16. Complete the table using information in *Exploring Uses of Bases* on
    page 98 and in Figure 15 on page 99.

Common Bases		
Base	**Formula**	**Use**
Sodium hydroxide		
Calcium hydroxide		
Magnesium hydroxide		
Ammonia		
Calcium oxide		

© Prentice-Hall, Inc.

SECTION 3-3 Acids and Bases in Solution (pages 100–105)

This section explains what kinds of ions acids and bases form in water. It also describes what happens when acids and bases react.

▶ Acids in Solution (pages 100–101)

1. What is a hydrogen ion (H⁺)? _____

_____

_____

2. What forms when hydrochloric acid reacts with water? _____

_____

3. Any substance that forms hydrogen ions (H⁺) in water can be called a(n)

_____.

▶ Bases in Solution (page 101)

4. What is a hydroxide ion (OH⁻)? _____

_____

_____

5. Any substance that forms hydroxide ions (OH⁻) in water can be called

a(n) _____.

▶ Strengths of Acids and Bases (page 102)

6. Circle the letter of each sentence that is true about the strength of acids and bases.

   a. Strong bases produce more OH⁻ ions than weak bases.

   b. Weak acids produce more OH⁻ ions than strong acids.

   c. Strong acids produce more H⁺ ions than weak acids.

   d. Weak bases produce more H⁺ ions than strong bases.

© Prentice-Hall, Inc.

CHAPTER 3, Everyday Changes in Substances *(continued)*

7. Circle the letter of each strong acid or strong base.

   a. ammonia   **b.** sulfuric acid   **c.** lye   **d.** citric acid

8. Is the following sentence true or false? A strong acid is safe as long as

   it's in a dilute solution. _____

▶ Measuring pH (pages 102–103)

9. What is the pH scale? _____

   _____

   _____

10. On the scale below, add labels to show the pH of these substances: milk,
    soap, water, vinegar, lemon, and ammonia.

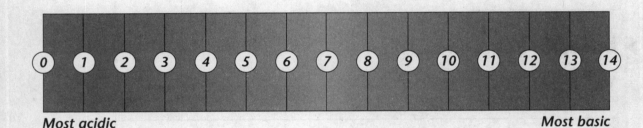

Most acidic   Most basic

11. When the pH of a solution is low, is the concentration of hydrogen ions

    high or low? _____

12. Circle the letter of each sentence that is true about pH.

    a. A pH lower than 7 is acidic.

    b. A pH of 7 is neutral.

    c. A pH lower than 7 is basic.

    d. A pH higher than 7 is acidic.

▶ Acid Rain—A Chemical Phenomenon (page 104)

13. Rain that is more acidic than normal rainwater is called

    _____.

© Prentice-Hall, Inc.

14. Why is acid rain a problem? _____

_____

_____

_____

▶ Acid-Base Reactions (page 104)

15. A reaction between an acid and a base is called a(n)

_____.

16. Is the following sentence true or false? An acid-base mixture is always

more acidic than the starting solutions were. _____

▶ Products of Acid-Base Reactions (page 105)

17. What is a salt? _____

_____

18. What two substances does a neutralization reaction produce?

    a. _____

    b. _____

19. Circle the letter of the salt that is used as a de-icer for roads and
walkways.

    a. KCl   **b.** ammonium nitrate   **c.** $CaCO_3$ **d.** calcium chloride

 Reading Skill Practice

When you read about complex topics, writing an outline can help you organize and understand the material. Outline Section 3–3 by using the headings and subheadings as topics and subtopics of your outline and then writing the most important details under each topic. Do your work on a separate sheet of paper.

© Prentice-Hall, Inc.

CHAPTER 3, Everyday Changes in Substances *(continued)*

SECTION 3-4   Digestion and pH
(pages 108–110)

This section explains why it is necessary for your body to digest food. It also explains how pH affects digestion.

▶ The Function of Your Digestive System (pages 108–109)

1. The process that breaks down the complex molecules of food into

   smaller molecules is called _____.

2. Why must foods be broken down in your body? _____

   _____

   _____

   _____

3. Complete the table about the two processes of digestion.

Digestion	
Digestive Process	**Description**
Mechanical digestion	
Chemical digestion	

4. Substances that speed up chemical reactions in living things are called

   _____.

5. Circle the letter of each sentence that is true about digestive enzymes.

   a. Enzymes require just the right temperature and pH to work.

   b. The pH must be neutral for enzymes to work.

   c. Some enzymes require the pH to be high.

   d. Some enzymes require the pH to be low.

© Prentice-Hall, Inc.

▶ pH in the Digestive System (pages 109–110)

6. Is the following sentence true or false? The pH is not the same in all

parts of the digestive system. _____

7. What is amylase? _____

_____

_____

8. Amylase works best when the pH is near _____.

9. The stomach starts digestion of which kind of foods? _____

_____

_____

10. What occurs in your stomach that drops the pH to a very acidic level of

about 2? _____

_____

11. What does pepsin do? _____

_____

_____

12. Pepsin works most effectively when the pH is _____.

13. Where does food go when it leaves the stomach? _____

_____

14. What causes the pH in the small intestine to rise to about 8? _____

_____

_____

15. Is the following sentence true or false? Enzymes in the small intestine

work best in a slightly basic solution. _____

16. Most chemical digestion ends in the _____.

© Prentice-Hall, Inc.

CHAPTER 3, Everyday Changes in Substances *(continued)*

WordWise

Match each definition in the left column with the correct term in the right column. Then write the number of each term in the appropriate box below. Next, add up the numbers in each column, row, and two diagonals. All the sums should be the same.

A. A very well-mixed mixture

B. The part of a solution that is present in the smaller amount

C. A compound that changes color in the presence of an acid or a base

D. A substance that turns blue litmus paper red

E. A mixture that has a lot of solute dissolved in it

F. A negatively charged, polyatomic ion

G. A process that breaks down the complex molecules of food into smaller molecules

H. The part of a solution that is present in the larger amount

I. Any ionic compound that can form from the neutralization of an acid with a base

1. solute

2. digestion

3. hydroxide ion (OH⁻)

4. salt

5. concentrated solution

6. solution

7. acid

8. indicator

9. solvent

= _____

A _____	B _____	C _____
D _____	E _____	F _____
G _____	H _____	I _____

= _____

= _____

= _____

= _____

= _____   = _____   = _____   = _____

_____

© Prentice-Hall, Inc.

CHAPTER 4

MOTION AND FORCES

••

SECTION 4–1 **The Nature of Force and Motion**
(pages 116–121)

This section explains how balanced and unbalanced forces are related to the motion of an object. It also explains Newton's first law of motion.

▶ What Is a Force? (pages 116–117)

1. In science, a force is _____.

2. When one object pushes or pulls another object, the first object is

   _____ a force on the second object.

3. Circle the letters of the two ways that forces are described.

   a. direction   **b.** velocity   **c.** strength   **d.** acceleration

▶ Unbalanced Forces and Motion (pages 117–118)

4. When two forces act in the same direction, they _____ together.

5. Adding a force acting in one direction to a force acting in another

   direction is the same as adding a(n) _____ number and

   a(n) _____ number.

6. Look at Figure 1 on page 117. What does the width of the arrows tell you

   about the forces they represent? _____

   _____

7. The overall force on an object after all the forces are added together is

   called the _____.

© Prentice-Hall, Inc.

CHAPTER 4, Motion and Forces *(continued)*

8. The illustrations to the right represent ways that two forces can combine. Draw lines from the left column to the right column to show the result of each combination.

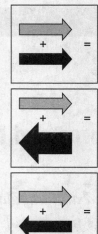 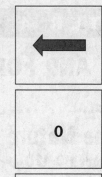

9. Unbalanced forces can cause an object to do three things. What are they?

_____

_____

10. Is the following sentence true or false? Unbalanced forces acting on an

object will change the object's motion. _____

11. Circle the letter of each sentence that is true about unbalanced forces.

    a. When two forces act in opposite directions, the net force is the difference between the two forces.

    b. When two forces act in the same direction, the net force is the difference between the two forces.

    c. When two forces act in opposite directions, the net force is equal to the greater force.

    d. When two forces act in the same direction, the net force is the sum of the two individual forces.

▶ Balanced Forces and Motion (page 118)

12. Equal forces acting on one object in opposite directions are called

_____ .

© Prentice-Hall, Inc.

13. Is the following sentence true or false? Balanced forces acting on an object will change the object's motion. _____

14. When you add equal forces exerted in opposite directions, the net force is _____.

▶ Newton's First Law of Motion (pages 120–121)

15. Is the following sentence true or false? Once an object is in its natural resting place, it cannot move by itself. _____

16. Is the following sentence true or false? Galileo suggested that once an object is in motion, no push or pull is needed to keep it moving.

_____

17. What is inertia? _____

_____

18. What is Newton's first law of motion? _____

_____

_____

_____

19. Newton's first law of motion is also called the law of _____.

20. What explains why you continue moving forward if you are in a car that suddenly stops? _____

21. What is mass? _____

_____

22. What is the SI unit of mass? _____

23. The amount of inertia an object has depends on its _____.

24. How can mass be defined in terms of inertia? _____

_____

© Prentice-Hall, Inc.

CHAPTER 4, Motion and Forces *(continued)*

SECTION 4-2 | Force, Mass, and Acceleration (pages 124-126)

This section explains how force and mass are related to the acceleration of an object.

▶ **Newton's Second Law of Motion (pages 124–125)**

1. What is Newton's second law of motion? _____

   _____

   _____

   _____

2. What is the equation that describes the relationship among quantities of force, mass, and acceleration?

   _____

3. Circle the letters of two answers below that are ways to write units of force.

   a. m/s^2 **b.** N   **c.** $kg \cdot ms^2$ **d.** 1 kg

4. Using Newton's second law, write an equation you can use to find acceleration.

   _____

▶ **Changes in Force and Mass (page 126)**

5. How does an increase of force affect acceleration? _____

   _____

   _____

6. What are two ways you can increase the acceleration of an object?

   _____

   _____

© Prentice-Hall, Inc.

7. How does an increase of mass affect acceleration? _____

_____

8. Is the following sentence true or false? One way to increase the force used to pull a wagon is to decrease the mass in the wagon.

_____

• •

SECTION 4–3 **Friction and Gravity**
(pages 127–133)

This section describes the effects of friction on surfaces that rub against each other. It also describes how gravity acts between objects in the universe.

▶ **Friction** (pages 128–129)

1. Is the following sentence true or false? When two surfaces rub together, the irregularities of one surface get caught on those of the other surface.

_____

2. What is friction? _____

_____

_____

3. Friction acts in a direction _____ to the object's direction of motion.

4. The strength of the force of friction depends on what two factors?

_____

_____

5. How is friction useful in helping you walk? _____

_____

_____

© Prentice-Hall, Inc.

CHAPTER 4, Motion and Forces (continued)

6. How does friction help an automobile move? _____

_____

_____

7. Complete the following table about the different kinds of friction.

Kinds of Friction	
Kind of Friction	**Friction Occurs When . . .**
	An object moves through a fluid
	Solid surfaces slide over each other
	An object rolls over a surface

8. Which kind of friction requires more force to overcome, rolling friction

or sliding friction? _____

9. What kind of friction occurs when moving parts have ball bearings?

_____

10. How does oil between machine parts reduce friction? _____

_____

_____

▶ Gravity (pages 130–132)

11. The force that pulls objects toward Earth is called _____.

12. When is an object said to be in free fall? _____

_____

_____

13. Near the surface of Earth, what is the acceleration of an object due to

the force of gravity? _____

14. An object that is thrown is called a(n) _____.

© Prentice-Hall, Inc.

15. Is the following sentence true or false? An object that is dropped will hit the ground before an object that is thrown horizontally. _____

16. Objects falling through air experience a type of fluid friction called

_____.

17. Is the following sentence true or false? The greater the surface area of an object, the greater the air resistance. _____

18. On the diagram below, draw arrows that show the forces acting on the falling acorn. Label each arrow with the name of the force.

19. The greatest velocity a falling object reaches is called _____.

20. What is weight? _____

_____

_____

21. How is weight different than mass? _____

_____

_____

_____

22. Weight is usually measured in _____.

© Prentice-Hall, Inc.

CHAPTER 4, Motion and Forces *(continued)*

▶ Universal Gravitation (pages 132–133)

23. Is the following sentence true or false? The force that makes an apple fall to the ground is the same force that keeps Earth orbiting the sun.

_____

24. What does the universal law of gravitation state? _____

_____

_____

25. Is the following sentence true or false? On the moon, your mass would be less than it is on Earth. _____

26. The force of attraction between two objects varies with what two factors? _____

_____

SECTION 4–4 Action and Reaction (pages 134–139)

This section explains Newton's third law of motion. It also explains the law of conservation of momentum.

▶ Newton's Third Law of Motion (pages 134–136)

1. What is Newton's third law of motion? _____

_____

_____

_____

2. What did Newton call the force exerted by the first object on a second object? _____

© Prentice-Hall, Inc.

3. What did Newton call the force exerted by the second object back on

the first object? _____

4. The action and reaction forces in any situation will always be

_____ and _____.

5. Complete the flowchart below, which describes how a squid moves
through water.

Newton's Squid

A squid expels water out its back end. This is the

_____ force.

↓

The water expelled out of the back end of the squid pushes

back, exerting an equal and _____ force

on the squid. This is the _____ force.

↓

The squid moves _____ through the
water as a result of the reaction force.

6. Explain why the equal action and reaction forces do not cancel each

other when one person hits a ball. _____

_____

_____

_____

_____

_____

© Prentice-Hall, Inc.

CHAPTER 4, Motion and Forces *(continued)*

▶ Momentum (page 137)

7. The product of an object's mass and velocity is its _____.

8. What is the equation you use to determine the momentum of an object?

_____

9. What is the unit of measurement for momentum? _____

_____

▶ Conservation of Momentum (pages 138–139)

10. What does the law of conservation of momentum state? _____

_____

_____

11. Suppose a train car moving down a track at 10 m/s hits another train car that is not moving. Explain how momentum is conserved after the

collision. _____

_____

_____

 Reading Skill Practice

A flowchart can help you remember the order in which a series of events occurs. Create a flowchart that describes how momentum is conserved when a moving train car collides with another moving train car. See your textbook on page 138 . The first step in the flowchart will be this: One train car moves down a track at 10 m/s. The last step in the flowchart will be this: Momentum is conserved. Do your work on a separate sheet of paper. For more information about flowcharts, see page 661 in the Skills Handbook of your textbook.

© Prentice-Hall, Inc.

• •

SECTION 4-5 Forces in Fluids (pages 140-150)

This section explains what causes pressure in fluids. It also explains Pascal's principle and Bernoulli's principle.

▶ What Is Pressure? (pages 140–141)

1. What do snowshoes do that makes it easier for the person wearing them to travel in deep snow? _____

_____

_____

_____

_____

2. Is the following sentence true or false? Force and pressure are the same thing. _____

3. What is pressure equal to? _____

_____

_____

4. Circle the letter of the term that is an SI unit of pressure.

   a. newton   **b.** liter

   c. weight   **d.** pascal

5. Circle the letter of the *two* answers below that are equal to each other.

   a. 1 Pa   **b.** 1 N/cm^2

   c. 1 N/m^2 **d.** 1 N

6. Is the following sentence true or false? You can produce a lower pressure by decreasing the area a force acts on. _____

© Prentice-Hall, Inc.

CHAPTER 4, Motion and Forces *(continued)*

▶ Fluid Pressure *(page 142)*

7. A substance that can flow easily is a(n) _____.

8. Circle the letter of each of the following that are fluids.

    a. helium gas   **b.** liquid water   **c.** ice   **d.** air

9. Describe how molecules move in fluids. _____

    _____

    _____

    _____

10. What causes the pressure exerted by a fluid? _____

    _____

    _____

11. The pressure exerted by a fluid is the total force exerted by the fluid

    divided by the _____ over which the force is exerted.

▶ Pascal's Principle *(page 143)*

12. What happens to the pressure in a bottle of water if you press the

    stopper at the top down farther? _____

    _____

13. What is the relationship known as Pascal's principle? _____

    _____

    _____

    _____

▶ Equilibrium in a Volcano *(page 144)*

14. Is the following sentence true or false? A volcano that is in equilibrium

    erupts. _____

© Prentice-Hall, Inc.

▶ Force Pumps and Blood Flow (page 144)

15. What does a force pump do? _____

_____

_____

16. Describe the heart in terms of force pumps. _____

_____

_____

_____

▶ Using Pascal's Principle (page 145)

17. Suppose you push down on a small piston that is connected to a confined fluid, and another piston with the same area is connected by a U-shaped tube to the confined fluid. How much fluid pressure will the

second piston experience compared to the first? _____

_____

18. In a hydraulic system, how is the force applied on a small surface area

multiplied? _____

_____

_____

_____

▶ Pascal's Principle in Nature (page 148)

19. The tube feet of a sea star take advantage of what principle to move

around? _____

20. When a sea star contracts different muscles, it changes the

_____ in the fluid of its tube foot.

21. The _____ a sea star exerts on the fluid in its system
causes the tube foot to either push down or pull up on its sucker.

© Prentice-Hall, Inc.

CHAPTER 4, Motion and Forces (continued)

▶ Bernoulli's Principle (pages 148–150)

22. Is the following sentence true or false? The faster a fluid moves, the

more pressure the fluid exerts. _____

23. What does Bernoulli's principle state? _____

_____

_____

24. Is the following sentence true or false? A faster-moving fluid exerts less

pressure than a slower-moving fluid. _____

25. On the illustration of a wing below, draw arrows that show the path of
air above and below the wing.

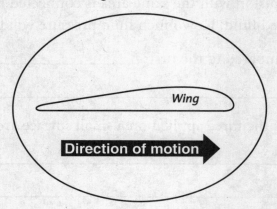

26. Air that moves over the top of an airplane wing must travel farther
than air that moves along the bottom of the wing. As a result, the air

moving over the top exerts less _____ than the air
moving along the bottom.

27. What is lift? _____

_____

28. How do differences in air pressure cause smoke to rise up a chimney?

_____

_____

© Prentice-Hall, Inc.

WordWise

Use the clues to help you find the key terms from Chapter 4 hidden in the puzzle below. The terms may occur vertically, horizontally, or diagonally.

1. A _____ is a push or pull.
2. The overall force on an object after all forces are added together is called the _____ force.
3. The tendency of an object to resist change in its motion is called _____ .
4. One _____ equals the force required to accelerate 1 kilogram of mass at 1 meter per second per second.
5. The force that one surface exerts on another when the two rub against each other is called _____ .
6. When solid surfaces slide over each other, the kind of friction that occurs is _____ friction.

7. A substance that can flow easily is called a(n) _____ .
8. The force that pulls objects toward Earth is _____ .
9. When the only force acting on a falling object is gravity, the object is said to be in _____ fall.
10. Objects falling through air experience a type of fluid friction called _____ resistance.
11. The _____ of an object is the product of its mass and velocity.
12. The force exerted on a surface divided by the area over which the force is exerted is called _____ .

```
s  q  m  o  m  e  n  t  u  m
m  f  g  i  n  e  r  t  i  a
a  o  r  l  i  o  l  n  g  f
s  r  a  i  q  a  z  y  n  r
w  c  v  p  .c  f  r  e  e  i
g  e  i  w  h  t  a  e  w  c
u  p  t  f  l  u  i  d  t  t
i  e  y  c  n  i  r  o  o  i
n  s  l  i  d  i  n  g  n  o
p  r  e  s  s  u  r  e  e  n
```

© Prentice-Hall, Inc.

CHAPTER 4, Motion and Forces *(continued)*

MathWise

For the problems below, show your calculations on another sheet of paper. Write the answers for the problems on the lines below.

▶ Newton's Second Law of Motion (pages 124–126)

1. Force = 65 kg × 3ms^2 = _____

2. A 250-kg trailer is being pulled by a truck. The force causes the trailer to accelerate at 4 m/s^2. What is the net force that causes this acceleration?

Answer: _____

▶ Weight and Mass (page 132)

3. Weight = 45 kg × 9.8 m/s^2 = _____

4. What is the weight of a rock that has a mass of 7 kg?

Answer: _____

▶ Momentum (page 137)

5. Momentum = 5 kg × 6.5 m/s = _____

6. A baseball (mass = 0.14 kg) travels at 7 m/s, while a basketball (mass = 0.5 kg) moves at 3 m/s. Which has the greater momentum?

_____

_____

▶ Calculating Pressure (page 141)

1. Pressure = $\dfrac{20 \text{ N}}{10 \text{ m}^2}$ = _____

2. A force of 25 N is exerted on a surface with an area of 5 m^2. What is the pressure on that area?

Answer: _____

© Prentice-Hall, Inc.

CHAPTER 5

WORK AND MACHINES

• •

SECTION 5–1 **What Is Work?**
(pages 156–159)

This section explains the scientific meaning of work and describes how to calculate the work done on an object.

▶ **The Meaning of Work** (pages 156–158)

1. In scientific terms, when do you do work? _____

_____

_____

_____

2. Complete the following table by classifying each example as either work or no work.

Work?	
Example	**Work or No Work?**
You pull your books out of your book bag.	
You lift a bin of newspapers.	
You push on a car stuck in the snow.	
You hold a heavy piece of wood in place.	
You pull a sled through the snow.	
You hold a bag of groceries.	

3. In order for you to do work on an object, the object must move some

_____ as a result of your force.

© Prentice-Hall, Inc.

CHAPTER 5, Work and Machines *(continued)*

4. Explain why you don't do any work when you carry an object at a

   constant velocity. _____

   _____

   _____

   _____

5. When you pull a sled through the snow, why does only part of your

   force do work? _____

   _____

   _____

   _____

▶ **Calculating Work** (pages 158–159)

6. Is the following sentence true or false? Lifting a heavier object demands

   greater force than lifting a lighter object. _____

7. Is the following sentence true or false? Moving an object a shorter
   distance requires more work than moving an object a greater distance.

   _____

8. The amount of work you do depends on both the amount of

   _____ you exert and the _____ the object

   moves.

9. What formula do you use to determine the amount of work done on an

   object? _____

10. What is the SI unit of work? _____

11. What is the amount of work you do when you exert a force of 1 newton

    to move an object a distance of 1 meter? _____

© Prentice-Hall, Inc.

SECTION 5–2 Mechanical Advantage and Efficiency
(pages 160–165)

This section explains how machines make work easier and describes how to calculate how efficient a machine is.

▶ What Is a Machine? (pages 160–162)

1. What is a machine? _____
   _____
   _____

2. Is the following sentence true or false? A machine decreases the amount
   of work needed to do a job. _____

3. Circle the letter of each sentence that is true about how a machine makes
   work easier.
   a. A machine makes work easier by multiplying force you exert.
   b. A machine makes work easier by reducing the amount of force needed
   to do the job.
   c. A machine makes work easier by multiplying the distance over which
   you exert force.
   d. A machine makes work easier by changing the direction in which you
   exert force.

4. The force you exert on a machine is called the _____.

5. The force exerted by the machine is called the _____.

6. Is the following sentence true or false? In some machines, the output
   force is greater than the input force. _____

7. If a machine allows you to use less force to do some amount of work, then
   you must apply the input force over a greater _____.

8. Is the following sentence true or false? In some machines, the output
   force is less than the input force. _____

© Prentice-Hall, Inc.

CHAPTER 5, Work and Machines *(continued)*

9. Write labels on the illustration below to show which arrow represents the input force and which represents the output force.

▶ Mechanical Advantage *(page 163)*

10. What is a machine's mechanical advantage? _____

_____

_____

11. What is the formula you use to determine the mechanical advantage of a machine?

_____

12. In a machine that has a mechanical advantage of more than 1, the

_____ force is greater than the _____ force.

▶ Efficiency of Machines *(pages 164–165)*

13. In any machine, some work is wasted overcoming _____.

14. The comparison of a machine's output work to its input work is

_____.

15. What is the formula you use to calculate the efficiency of a machine?

_____

© Prentice-Hall, Inc.

16. The mechanical advantage that a machine provides in a real situation is

called the _____ mechanical advantage.

17. The mechanical advantage of a machine without friction is called the

machine's _____ mechanical advantage.

📖 Reading Skill Practice

By looking carefully at photographs and illustrations in textbooks, you can help yourself
understand better what you have read. Look carefully at Figure 5 on page 161. What important
idea does this illustration communicate?

SECTION 5-3

Simple Machines
(pages 168-178)

*This section describes the six kinds of simple machines. It also explains how to
calculate the ideal mechanical advantage for each simple machine.*

▶ Introduction (page 168)

1. What are the six basic kinds of simple machines?

a. _____ b. _____ c. _____

d. _____ e. _____ f. _____

▶ Inclined Plane (pages 169–170)

2. What is an inclined plane? _____

_____

3. What formula do you use to determine the ideal mechanical advantage
of an inclined plane?

_____

© Prentice-Hall, Inc.

CHAPTER 5, Work and Machines *(continued)*

4. Circle the letter of each sentence that is true about inclined planes.

   a. The necessary input force is less than the output force.

   b. A ramp is an example of an inclined plane.

   c. The necessary input force is more than the output force.

   d. An inclined plane allows you to exert your force over a longer distance.

5. You can increase the _____ of an inclined plane by decreasing the friction.

▶ Wedge (page 170)

6. What is a wedge? _____

   _____

   _____

7. Is the following sentence true or false? In a wedge, the inclined plane itself moves. _____

8. Is the following sentence true or false? A wedge multiples force to do the job. _____

▶ Screws (page 171)

9. What is a screw? _____

   _____

10. A spiral inclined plane forms the _____ of a screw.

11. When using a screwdriver to twist a screw into a piece of wood, where is the input force applied and where is the output force exerted?

   _____

   _____

   _____

© Prentice-Hall, Inc.

SECTION 5-4 **Machines in Human Systems**
(pages 182-184)

This section describes how the body uses natural levers and wedges.

▶ Body Systems—Living Levers (pages 182-184)

1. What do most of the levers in your body consist of? _____

_____

2. Your muscles are attached to your bones by tough connective tissue

called _____.

3. In a living lever in your body, what acts as the lever's fulcrum?

_____

_____

4. On the illustration of a living lever, label each arrow to show where the
input force and the output force are located. Also show where the
fulcrum is located.

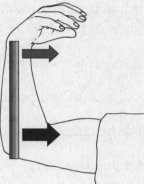

▶ Working Wedges (page 184)

5. What simple machines do your incisors resemble? _____

6. Explain how your front teeth are like an ax. _____

_____

_____

_____

© Prentice-Hall, Inc.

CHAPTER 5, Work and Machines *(continued)*

WordWise

Complete the sentences by using one of the scrambled words below.

Word Bank

lelyup xela oounmpdc fiienycef ttuuop veelr

euojl deegw tupni rwko wecrs clruumf iclndeni enihcam

A device that is thick at one end and tapers to a thin edge at the other end is a(n)

_____.

A machine that utilizes two or more simple machines is called a(n) _____
machine.

The force exerted by a machine is called the _____ force.

The fixed point that a lever pivots around is called the _____.

You do _____ on an object when you exert a force on the object that
causes the object to move some distance.

A wheel and _____ is a simple machine made of two circular or
cylindrical objects that are fastened together and that rotate around a common axis.

The _____ of a machine compares the output work to the input work.

A rigid bar that is free to pivot, or rotate, about a fixed point is a(n) _____.

The force you exert on a machine is called the _____ force.

A(n) _____ plane is a flat, slanted surface.

A grooved wheel with a rope wrapped around it is a(n) _____.

A device with which you can do work in a way that is easier or more effective is a(n)

_____.

The SI unit of work is called the _____.

A(n) _____ can be thought of as an inclined plane wrapped around a
cylinder.

© Prentice-Hall, Inc.

MathWise

For the problems below, show your calculations. If you need more space, use another sheet of paper. Write the answers for the problems on the lines below.

▶ Calculating Work (pages 158–159)

1. Work = 10 N × 35 m = _____

2. An elevator lifts a man with a weight of 500 N up three floors, or 30 m. How much work did the elevator do?

   Answer: _____

▶ Mechanical Advantage (page 163)

3. Mechanical advantage = $\dfrac{60 \text{ N}}{15 \text{ N}}$ = _____

4. Suppose you exert of force of 2,800 N to lift a desk up onto a porch. But if you use a ramp, you need to exert a force of only 1,400 N to push it up the ramp onto the porch. What is the mechanical advantage of the ramp?

   Answer: _____

▶ Calculating Efficiency (pages 164–165)

5. Efficiency = $\dfrac{100 \text{ J}}{200 \text{ J}}$ × 100% = _____

6. You do 4,000 J of work using a sledge hammer. The sledge hammer does 3,000 J of work on the spike. What is the efficiency of the sledge hammer?

   Answer: _____

© Prentice-Hall, Inc.

CHAPTER 5, Work and Machines *(continued)*

▶ Advantage of an Inclined Plane (page 169)

7. Ideal mechanical advantage $= \dfrac{8 \text{ m}}{2 \text{ m}} =$ _____

8. Suppose you built a ramp to the front door of the post office for people using wheel chairs. The post office door is 3 m above the level of the sidewalk. The ramp you build is 15 m long. What is the ideal mechanical advantage of your ramp?

   Answer: _____

▶ Advantage of a Lever (page 172)

9. Ideal mechanical advantage $= \dfrac{4 \text{ m}}{2 \text{ m}} =$ _____

10. Suppose you held the handles of a wheel barrow 2.4 m from where they are attached to the wheel. The heavy stone in the wheel barrow was 1.2 m from the wheel. What is the ideal mechanical advantage of the wheel barrow?

    Answer: _____

▶ Advantage of a Wheel and Axle (pages 175–176)

11. Ideal mechanical advantage $= \dfrac{36 \text{ cm}}{3 \text{ cm}} =$ _____

12. Suppose the radius of your bicycle's wheel is 30 cm. The radius of the bicycle's axle is just 5 cm. What is the ideal mechanical advantage of that wheel and axle?

    Answer: _____

© Prentice-Hall, Inc.

CHAPTER 6

ENERGY AND POWER

· ·

SECTION 6-1 **The Nature of Energy**
(pages 190–195)

This section explains how work and energy are related. It also identifies the two basic kinds of energy and describes some different forms of energy.

▶ What Is Energy? (pages 190–191)

1. The ability to do work or cause change is called _____.

2. Why can work be thought of as the transfer of energy? _____
_____
_____

▶ Kinetic Energy (pages 191–192)

3. What are the two general kinds of energy?

   a. _____   b. _____

4. What is kinetic energy? _____

5. The kinetic energy of an object depends on both its _____

   and its _____.

6. Kinetic energy increases as velocity _____.

7. What formula do you use to calculate kinetic energy?

_____

8. Because velocity is squared in the kinetic energy equation, doubling an

   object's velocity will _____ its kinetic energy.

© Prentice-Hall, Inc.

CHAPTER 6, Energy and Power (continued)

▶ Potential Energy (pages 192–193)

9. What is potential energy? _____

_____

10. What is the potential energy called that is associated with objects that

can be stretched or compressed? _____

11. What is potential energy called that depends on height? _____

_____

12. What is the formula you use to determine the gravitational potential

energy of an object? _____

13. Is the following sentence true or false? The greater the height of an

object, the greater its gravitational potential energy. _____

▶ Different Forms of Energy (pages 194–195)

14. What is mechanical energy? _____

_____

15. What is thermal energy? _____

_____

_____

16. Is the following sentence true or false? When the thermal energy of an

object increases, its particles move faster. _____

17. The potential energy stored in chemical bonds that hold chemical

compounds together is called _____.

18. What kind of energy is stored in the foods you eat? _____

19. The energy that moving electric charges carry is called

_____ energy.

© Prentice-Hall, Inc.

20. What kind of energy is stored in the nucleus of an atom?

_____

21. Complete the table below on the different forms of energy.

Different Forms of Energy	
Form of Energy	**Examples**
Mechanical energy	
Thermal energy	
Chemical energy	
Electrical energy	
Electromagnetic energy	
Nuclear energy	

 ## Reading Skill Practice

Outlining is a way to help yourself understand better and remember what you have read. Write an outline of Section 6–1, *The Nature of Energy.* In your outline, copy the headings in the textbook. Under each heading, write the main idea of that part of the section. Then list the details that support, or back up, the main idea.

© Prentice-Hall, Inc.

SECTION 6-2 **Energy Conversion and Conservation** (pages 198-203)

This section explains how different forms of energy are related and describes the law of conservation of energy.

▶ **Conversions Between Forms of Energy** (page 199)

1. A change from one form of energy to another is called a(n)

_____.

CHAPTER 6, Energy and Power *(continued)*

2. Is the following sentence true or false? Most forms of energy can be converted into other forms. _____

3. Describe the conversion of chemical energy to mechanical energy in your body. _____

_____

_____

▶ Kinetic and Potential Energy (pages 200–201)

4. When you throw an object up into the air, what kind of energy increases as its height increases? _____

5. As an object falls from its greatest height, what kind of energy increases and what kind of energy decreases? _____

_____

_____

6. On the diagram of a moving pendulum, label the places where the pendulum has maximum potential energy and where it has maximum kinetic energy.

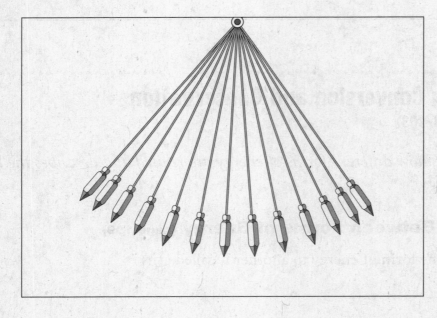

© Prentice-Hall, Inc.

▶ Conservation of Energy (pages 202–203)

7. What does the law of conservation of energy state? _____

_____

_____

8. Friction converts mechanical energy to _____ energy.

9. Explain why no machine is 100 percent efficient? _____

_____

10. How did Albert Einstein's theory of relativity change the law of

conservation of energy? _____

_____

11. Is the following sentence true or false? Matter and energy together are

always conserved. _____

▶ Conserving Energy (page 203)

12. In environmental science, conserving energy means to _____

_____

13. In physical science, energy is conserved because _____

_____

· ·

SECTION 6-3 # Photosynthesis and Fossil Fuels
(pages 204–)

This section explains how photosynthesis is the source of the energy stored in fossil fuels. It also describes how energy is converted when fossil fuels are used.

▶ Photosynthesis (page 205)

1. Photosynthesis is the process through which plants make their own

_____.

© Prentice-Hall, Inc.

CHAPTER 6, Energy and Power *(continued)*

▶ The Nature of Light (page 205)

2. The source of energy on Earth is the _____.

3. What can occur when light strikes an object? _____

_____

_____

▶ Plants and Light (page 206)

4. The most abundant pigment in plants is _____.

▶ Energy Conversion in Photosynthesis (pages 206–208)

5. Plants and some other organisms convert the sun's radiant energy into

   chemical energy through the process of _____.

6. During the first stage of photosynthesis, chlorophyll and other

   pigments capture _____ energy.

7. Write the equation for photosynthesis using words.

_____

▶ Glucose and Stored Energy (page 208)

8. Is the following sentence true or false? During respiration, the chemical
   energy stored in glucose is converted into other forms of energy, such

   as mechanical energy or thermal energy. _____

▶ Fossil Fuels (pages 209–210)

9. Is the following sentence true or false? A fuel is a material that releases

   energy when it burns. _____

10. Circle the letter of each of the following that is a fossil fuel.

    a. coal   **b.** sunlight   **c.** petroleum   **d.** natural gas

© Prentice-Hall, Inc.

▶ Using Fossil Fuels (page 211)

11. How is the potential chemical energy of fossil fuels converted to other

forms? _____

12. The process of burning fossil fuels is known as _____.

13. What energy conversion occurs during combustion? _____

_____

14. In a modern coal-fired power plant, the mechanical energy of turbines

is converted into electrical energy by _____.

SECTION 6-4
Power
(pages 212-216)

This section describes how you calculate power and explains the difference between power and energy.

▶ What Is Power? (pages 212-213)

1. What is power? _____

_____

2. Is the following sentence true or false? You exert more power when you run up a flight of stairs than when you walk up the stairs.

_____

3. If one device is twice as powerful as another device, the more powerful

device can do _____ the amount of work in the same amount of time.

4. What is the formula you use to calculate power?

_____

5. Rewrite the equation for power in a way that shows what work equals.

_____

© Prentice-Hall, Inc.

CHAPTER 6, Energy and Power (continued)

6. 1 J/s = 1 _____

7. Is the following sentence true or false? Power is often measured in

larger units than watts. _____

8. 1 kilowatt = _____ watts

9. Is the following sentence true or false? An electric power plant produces

millions of kilowatts. _____

▶ Power and Energy (pages 214–215)

10. Is the following sentence true or false? Power is limited to situations in

which objects are moved. _____

11. Power is the _____ at which energy is transferred from
one object to another or converted from one form to another.

12. The power of a light bulb is the rate at which _____

energy is converted into _____ energy and

_____ energy.

13. Why is a 100-watt light bulb brighter than a 40-watt light bulb?

_____

_____

_____

▶ Horsepower (page 216)

14. Circle the letter of each sentence that is true about the unit known as
horsepower.

a. Horsepower is an SI unit of power.

b. James Watt used the word *horsepower* to compare the work of a
steam engine with the work of a horse.

c. People use the unit horsepower when talking about automobile engines.

d. 1 horsepower = 746 watts

© Prentice-Hall, Inc.

WordWise

Complete the following paragraphs using the list of words and phrases below. Each word or phrase is used only once.

Word Bank

law of conservation of energy   nuclear energy   kinetic energy

fossil fuels   electromagnetic energy   energy conversion   electrical energy

power   energy   mechanical energy   potential energy   chemical energy

In nature, things are constantly changing, and the identification of what causes changes is important in physical science. The ability to do work or cause change is called _____. There are two general kinds of energy. The energy of motion is called _____. Energy that is stored and held in readiness is called _____.

There are different forms of the two general kinds of energy. The energy associated with the motion or position of an object is _____. The potential energy stored in chemical bonds that hold chemical compounds together is _____. The energy that moving electric charges carry is _____. Visible light and other waves of energy are forms of _____. The energy stored in the nucleus of an atom is _____.

Most forms of energy can be converted into other forms. A change from one form of energy to another is called _____. Such changes from one form of energy to another do not mean any energy is lost. The _____ states that when one form of energy is converted to another, no energy is destroyed in the process.

A fuel is a material that stores chemical potential energy. For many purposes, we use _____, such as coal, petroleum, and natural gas. The energy conversions in modern coal-fired power plants result in the electricity you use for home electrical devices. You use these devices to do work. The rate at which work is done, or the amount of work done in a unit of time, is called _____.

© Prentice-Hall, Inc.

CHAPTER 6, Energy and Power *(continued)*

MathWise

For the problems below, show your calculations. If you need more space, use another sheet of paper. Write the answers for the problems on the lines below.

▶ Calculating Gravitational Potential Energy (page 193)

1. Gravitational potential energy = 25 N × 10 m = _____

2. A student stands at the edge of a diving board that is 3 m high. The student's weight is 350 N. What is the student's gravitational potential energy?

   Answer: _____

3. Gravitational potential energy = 60 kg × 9.8 m/s² × 5 m = _____

4. Suppose a boulder has a mass of 25 kg, and it is perched on the edge of a cliff that is 45 m high. What is the gravitational potential energy of the boulder?

   Answer: _____

▶ Calculating Power (pages 212–213)

5. Power = $\dfrac{5{,}000 \text{ N} \times 15 \text{ m}}{3 \text{ s}}$ = _____

6. You exert a force of 300 N to lift a box 2 m from the floor to a shelf in 3 s. How much power did you use?

   Answer: _____

© Prentice-Hall, Inc.

© Prentice-Hall, Inc.

CHAPTER 7

WEATHERING AND SOIL FORMATION

SECTION 7-1 Rocks and Weathering (pages 226-231)

This section describes how rocks are broken down by forces of weathering. The section also describes factors that determine how quickly weathering occurs.

▶ The Effects of Weathering (pages 226–227)

Match the process with its description.

Process	Description
_____ 1. weathering	**a.** Movement of rock particles by wind, water, ice, or gravity
_____ 2. erosion	**b.** Breaking down of rock and other substances at Earth's surface

3. Complete the concept map.

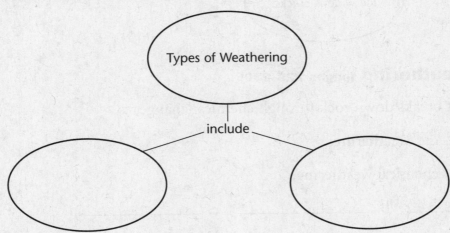

Types of Weathering

include

▶ Mechanical Weathering (pages 227–228)

4. The type of weathering in which rock is physically broken into smaller

pieces is called _____ weathering.

CHAPTER 7, Weathering and Soil Formation (continued)

5. List the forces of mechanical weathering.

a. _____   b. _____   c. _____

d. _____   e. _____

6. What is abrasion? _____

_____

_____

7. Complete the cycle diagram.

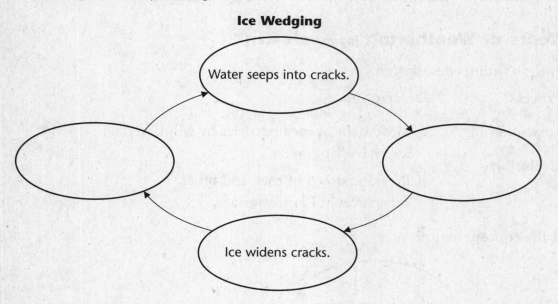

Ice Wedging

Water seeps into cracks.

Ice widens cracks.

▶ Chemical Weathering (pages 229–230)

8. The process that breaks down rock through chemical changes is

_____ weathering.

9. List the agents of chemical weathering.

a. _____   b. _____   c. _____

d. _____   e. _____

10. Is the following sentence true or false? Chemical weathering produces rock particles with the same mineral makeup as the rock they came

from. _____

© Prentice-Hall, Inc.

Match the agent of chemical weathering with the statement that is true about it.

Agent	Statement
_____ 11. water	a. It causes iron to rust.
_____ 12. oxygen	b. It's caused by pollution.
_____ 13. carbon dioxide	c. It's the most important agent.
	d. It forms carbonic acid.
_____ 14. living organisms	e. Lichens are one example.
_____ 15. acid rain	

16. Is the following sentence true or false? Water weathers rock by

dissolving it. _____

17. Oxygen weathers rock through a process called _____.

18. List two kinds of rock that are easily weathered by carbonic acid.

a. _____   b. _____

19. How do plants dissolve rock? _____

_____

_____

▶ Rate of Weathering (page 231)

20. The most important factors that determine the rate of weathering are

type of rock and _____.

21. Is the following sentence true or false? The minerals that make up a

rock determine how fast it weathers. _____

22. A rock that is full of tiny, connected air spaces is said to be

_____.

23. Why does a permeable rock weather chemically at a fast rate? _____

_____

_____

© Prentice-Hall, Inc.

CHAPTER 7, Weathering and Soil Formation *(continued)*

24. Why does chemical weathering occur more quickly in a hot climate?

_____

_____

_____

· ·

SECTION 7–2 **Soil Formation and Composition**
(pages 235–241)

This section explains how soil forms. The section also describes several features of soil, the living things found in soil, and the types of soil found in the United States.

▶ **Soil Formation** (page 235)

1. The loose, weathered material on Earth's surface in which plants can

grow is _____.

2. How does soil form? _____

_____

_____

3. The solid layer of rock beneath the soil is called _____.

▶ **Soil Composition** (page 236)

4. What two factors determine the type of rock particles and minerals in

any given soil? _____

_____

_____

5. List the three types of weathered rock particles found in soil.

a. _____ b. _____ c. _____

6. The decayed organic material in soil is called _____.

© Prentice-Hall, Inc.

▶ Soil Texture (page 236)

7. Circle the letter of the choice that lists soil particles from largest to smallest.

   a. sand, gravel, clay, silt

   b. gravel, sand, silt, clay

   c. gravel, silt, sand, clay

   d. gravel, sand, clay, silt

8. Soil that is made up of about equal parts of clay, sand, and silt is called

   _____.

▶ Soil Horizons (page 237)

Match the soil horizon with its makeup.

Soil Horizon	Makeup
_____ 9. A	a. Topsoil
_____ 10. B	b. Rock particles
_____ 11. C	c. Subsoil

12. Label each of the soil horizons shown in the three drawings as A, B, or C horizon.

Surface   *Surface*   *Surface*

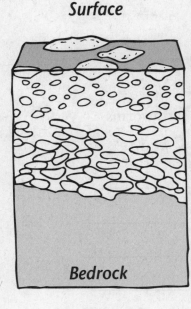
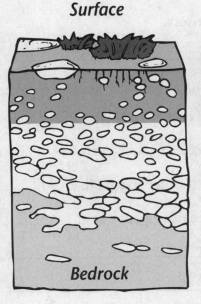
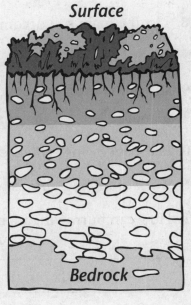

Bedrock   *Bedrock*   *Bedrock*

© Prentice-Hall, Inc.

CHAPTER 7, Weathering and Soil Formation (continued)

▶ Rate of Soil Formation (page 237)

13. Circle the letter of each sentence that is true about the rate of soil formation.

    a. It is faster in areas that are cold.

    b. It is slower in areas that are dry.

    c. It is faster with limestone than granite.

    d. It is unaffected by the type of rock being weathered.

▶ Life in Soil (pages 238–240)

14. How do soil organisms improve soil? _____

    _____

    _____

15. Is the following sentence true or false? Animals contribute most of the

    organic remains that form humus. _____

16. As plants shed leaves, they form a loose layer called _____.

17. Soil organisms that turn dead organic matter into humus are called

    _____.

18. List the main soil decomposers.

    a. _____ **b.** _____ **c.** _____ **d.** _____

19. Circle the letter of each choice that is an example of fungi.

    a. molds   **b.** mushrooms   **c.** bacteria   **d.** earthworms

20. Is the following sentence true or false? Earthworms do most of the

    work of mixing humus with other materials in soil. _____

21. How can burrowing mammals improve soil? _____

    _____

    _____

© Prentice-Hall, Inc.

▶ **Soil Types in the United States** (pages 240–241)

22. Circle the letter of each factor that scientists use to classify the different types of soil into groups.

    a. climate

    b. plant types

    c. soil composition

    d. size of animal populations

23. Is the following sentence true or false? The soil type of northeastern

    United States and Canada is southern forest soils. _____

 Reading Skill Practice

When you read a section that contains new or difficult material, identifying the sentence that best expresses the main topic under each heading can help you focus on the most important points. For each heading in Section 7–2, identify and copy the sentence that best expresses the main topic under that heading. Do your work on a separate sheet of paper.

SECTION 7–3

Soil Conservation
(pages 243–246)

This section explains why soil is valuable. The section also explains how soil can be damaged or lost, as well as how it can be conserved.

▶ **Introduction** (pages 243)

1. The thick mass of tough roots at the surface of the soil is called

   _____.

2. Prairie soils are among the most _____ soils in the world.

© Prentice-Hall, Inc.

CHAPTER 7, Weathering and Soil Formation *(continued)*

▶ The Value of Soil (pages 243–244)

3. Why is soil one of Earth's most valuable resources? _____

_____

_____

4. Circle the letter of each sentence that is true about soil.

   a. Soil is a nonrenewable resource.

   b. Soil formation takes a long time.

   c. Fertile soil is plentiful.

   d. Half of Earth has soils good for farming

5. List four reasons why farming is difficult in many areas on Earth.

   a. _____

   b. _____

   c. _____

   d. _____

▶ Soil Damage and Loss (page 244)

6. How can soil be damaged? _____

_____

7. How can soil be lost? _____

_____

8. Parts of Oklahoma and surrounding states that lost soil in the 1930s

   were called the _____.

▶ The Dust Bowl (page 244)

9. As you go from east to west across the Great Plains, the amount of

   rainfall _____ steadily.

© Prentice-Hall, Inc.

10. Why did the Dust Bowl occur? _____

_____

_____

_____

11. The soil lost from the Dust Bowl ended up in the _____
Ocean.

12. In the southern Plains states, the drought and topsoil loss lasted until

_____.

▶ Soil Conservation (page 246)

13. The management of soil to prevent its destruction is referred to as

_____.

14. Complete the concept map.

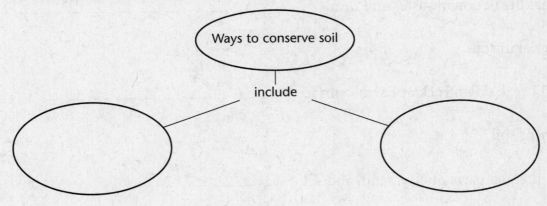

15. The practice of plowing fields along the curve of a slope is called

_____.

16. A method of farming that disturbs the soil and its plant cover as little

as possible is called _____.

© Prentice-Hall, Inc.

CHAPTER 7, Weathering and Soil Formation *(continued)*

WordWise

Test your knowledge of key terms from Chapter 7 by solving the clues. Then copy the numbered letters in order to reveal the hidden message.

Clues	Key Terms
Process of moving fragments of rock and soil	__ __ __ __ __ __ __ 1 2
Solid layer of rock beneath soil	__ __ __ __ __ __ __ 3 4
Thick mass of grass roots and soil	__ __ __ 5
Grinding away of rock by rock particles	__ __ __ __ __ __ __ __ 6
Loose layer of dead plant material on the soil surface	__ __ __ __ __ __ 7
Organisms that break down wastes and dead organisms	__ __ __ __ __ __ __ __ __ __ __ __ 8 9
Organic material in soil	__ __ __ __ __ 10
Processes that break down rock at Earth's surface	__ __ __ __ __ __ __ __ __ __ 11
Topmost layer of soil	__ __ __ __ __ __ __ 12
Soil with about equal parts of clay, sand, and silt	__ __ __ __ __ 13
Layer of soil beneath the topsoil	__ __ __ __ __ __ __ 14
Loose, weathered material in which plants can grow	__ __ __ __ 15

Hidden Message

__ __ __ __ __   __ __ __ __ __ __   __ __ __ __ .
1 2 3 4 5   6 7 8 9 10 11   12 13 14 15

© Prentice-Hall, Inc.

CHAPTER 8

EROSION AND DEPOSITION

SECTION 8–1 **Changing Earth's Surface** (pages 252-255)

This section explains how sediment is carried away and deposited elsewhere to wear down and build up Earth's surface. The section also describes ways that gravity moves sediment downhill.

▶ **Wearing Down and Building Up** (page 253)

1. What is erosion? _____

_____

_____

2. List the forces that cause erosion.

   a. _____ b. _____ c. _____

   d. _____ e. _____

3. The material moved by erosion is called _____.

4. Where does deposition occur? _____

_____

_____

▶ **Mass Movement** (pages 253–255)

5. Circle the letter of each sentence that is true about gravity.

   a. It pulls things toward Earth's center.

   b. It causes landslides.

   c. It causes mass movement.

   d. It is a force of erosion.

© Prentice-Hall, Inc.

CHAPTER 8, Erosion and Deposition *(continued)*

6. Is the following sentence true or false? A very destructive kind of

mass movement is creep. _____

7. Is the following sentence true or false? Mudflows and slump are

especially likely in soils high in clay. _____

8. Complete the concept map.

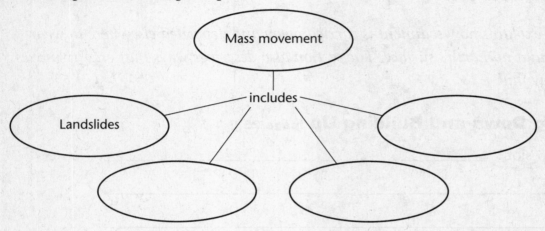

Match the type of mass movement with its description.

Mass Movement	Description
_____ **9.** landslide	**a.** Rock and soil suddenly slip down a slope in one large mass.
_____ **10.** mudflow	**b.** Rock and soil slide quickly down a slope.
_____ **11.** slump	**c.** Rock and soil move very slowly downhill.
_____ **12.** creep	**d.** A mixture of water, rock, and soil moves rapidly downhill.

Reading Skill Practice

When reading about cyclical processes, making a cycle diagram can help you understand how the processes are related. As you read or review Section 8-1, make a cycle diagram showing how the processes of weathering, erosion, and deposition are related. For more information on cycle diagrams, see page 661 in the Skills Handbook of the textbook. Do your work on a separate sheet of paper.

© Prentice-Hall, Inc.

●●●

SECTION 8-2 Water Erosion (pages 258-267)

This section describes how moving water erodes and deposits sediment to create landforms such as valleys and deltas.

▶ Runoff and Erosion (pages 259–260)

1. Is the following sentence true or false? Moving water is the major agent

   of erosion. _____

2. Water that moves over Earth's surface when it rains is called

   _____.

3. Fill in the first column of the table with the correct form of moving water.

Forms of Moving Water	
Form	**Description**
	Tiny groove in soil formed by runoff
	Channel that carries runoff after a rainstorm
	Channel with water continually flowing down a slope
	Large stream

4. Other than how people use the land, list four factors that determine the amount of runoff in an area.

   a. _____   b. _____

   c. _____   d. _____

5. Is the following sentence true or false? More runoff generally means less

   erosion. _____

▶ River Systems (pages 260–261)

6. A stream that flows into a larger stream is called a(n) _____.

© Prentice-Hall, Inc.

CHAPTER 8, Erosion and Deposition *(continued)*

7. The area of land from which a river and its tributaries collect water is

   the _____.

8. Is the following sentence true or false? The high ground between two

   drainage basins is called a divide. _____

▶ Erosion by Rivers (pages 261–262)

9. How do V-shaped valleys form? _____

   _____

   _____

10. When does a river develop meanders? _____

    _____

11. A meander that has been cut off from a river is called a(n)

    _____.

12. Identify and label each of the following landforms in the illustration:
    waterfall, oxbow lake, meander, flood plain, and V-shaped valley.

© Prentice-Hall, Inc.

▶ Deposits by Rivers (pages 263–265)

13. List two landforms created from deposits by rivers.

a. _____ b. _____

14. What is an alluvial fan? _____

_____

_____

15. Sediments deposited where a river flows into an ocean or lake form

a(n) _____.

16. What makes a river valley fertile? _____

_____

▶ Groundwater Erosion and Deposition (pages 266–267)

17. Underground water is called _____.

18. Is the following sentence true or false? Unlike moving surface water,

groundwater does not cause erosion. _____

19. How does groundwater cause chemical weathering of limestone?

_____

_____

20. Complete the compare/contrast table.

Groundwater Deposits In Limestone Caves	
Type of Deposit	**Where It Forms**
	Roof of cave
	Floor of cave

21. Is the following sentence true or false? An area where sinkholes are

common is said to have karst topography. _____

© Prentice-Hall, Inc.

CHAPTER 8, Erosion and Deposition *(continued)*

SECTION 8-3 **The Force of Moving Water**
(pages 271-274)

This section explains why moving water has energy and how it erodes and carries sediment. The section also identifies the factors that determine how much sediment a river can erode and carry.

▶ Work and Energy (pages 271–272)

1. The ability to do work or cause change is _____.

2. Energy that is stored for later use is called _____ energy.

3. Is the following statement true or false? Kinetic energy is the energy an object has due to its motion. _____

▶ How Water Erodes and Carries Sediment (page 272)

4. In what ways can sediment enter a river? _____

   _____

   _____

   _____

5. The wearing away of rock by a grinding action is called

   _____.

6. Is the following sentence true or false? Sediment in a river abrades the

   streambed and is abraded by the streambed in return. _____

7. The amount of sediment that a river carries is its _____.

8. Circle the letter of each sentence that is true about a river's sediment.

   a. Gravity and the force of the water cause sediment to move downstream.

   b. Most small sediments move by rolling and sliding along the bottom.

   c. Most large sediments move by bouncing.

   d. Some sediments are dissolved by the water and carried in solution.

© Prentice-Hall, Inc.

▶ Erosion and Sediment Load (pages 273–274)

9. Complete the concept map.

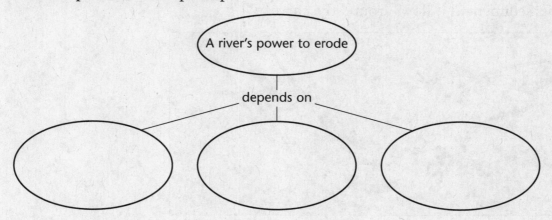

10. Is the following sentence true or false? When a river slows down and deposits its sediment load, smaller particles of sediment are deposited

first. _____

11. Circle the letter of each factor that increases the speed of a river.

   a. Steep slope   **b.** Low volume

   c. Deep streambed   **d.** Boulders in streambed

12. Circle the letter of each factor that decreases the speed of a river.

   a. Gentle slope   **b.** High volume

   c. Shallow streambed   **d.** Boulders in streambed

Match the term with its definition.

	Term	Definition
_____	**13.** flow	**a.** Movement of water every which way instead of downstream
_____	**14.** friction	**b.** Force that opposes the motion of one surface across another
_____	**15.** turbulence	**c.** Volume of water that moves past a point on a river in a given time

16. Is the following sentence true or false? Where a river flows in a straight line, the water flows faster along the river's sides than near the center.

_____

© Prentice-Hall, Inc.

CHAPTER 8, Erosion and Deposition (continued)

17. Label the drawing to show where the river erodes sediment and where it deposits sediment as it flows around the curve.

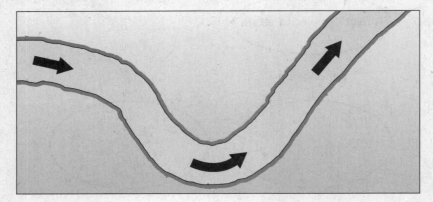

SECTION 8-4 Glaciers (pages 275-279)

This section describes huge ice masses, called glaciers. The section also describes the ice ages, a time when glaciers covered much of Earth. In addition, the section explains how glaciers form and move and how they cause erosion and deposition.

▶ Kinds of Glaciers (pages 275–276)

1. Any large mass of ice that moves slowly over land is a(n)

_____.

2. Circle the letter of each sentence that is true about valley glaciers.

   a. They are long, narrow glaciers.

   b. They are found on many high mountains.

   c. They are larger than continental glaciers.

   d. They follow river valleys.

3. Circle the letter of each sentence that is true about continental glaciers.

   a. They are larger than valley glaciers.

   b. They spread out over wide areas.

   c. They are found only in Antarctica.

   d. They cover 2 percent of Earth's land.

© Prentice-Hall, Inc.

▶ Ice Ages (page 276)

4. What are ice ages? _____

_____

_____

5. Is the following sentence true or false? The most recent ice age ended about 10,000 years ago. _____

6. Is the following sentence true or false? All of North America was covered by a continental glacier in the last ice age. _____

▶ How Glaciers Form and Move (page 276)

7. Where can glaciers form? _____

_____

8. When does gravity begin to pull a glacier downhill? _____

_____

_____

9. Complete the table.

How Glaciers Move	
Type of Glacier	**How It Moves**
	Flows in all directions
	Flows in a surge

▶ Glacial Erosion (pages 276–277)

10. List two processes by which glaciers erode the land.

a. _____   b. _____

11. Is the following sentence true or false? Plucking can move only small stones. _____

© Prentice-Hall, Inc.

CHAPTER 8, Erosion and Deposition *(continued)*

12. Describe the process of abrasion by a glacier and the effect abrasion has

    on the bedrock. _____

    _____

    _____

▶ Glacial Deposition (pages 277–279)

13. When does a glacier deposit the sediment it is carrying? _____

    _____

    _____

Match each type of glacial landform with its description.

Landform	Description
_____ **14.** till	**a.** Small depression formed by a chunk of ice and filled with water
_____ **15.** moraine	**b.** Mixture of sediments a glacier deposits on the surface
_____ **16.** terminal moraine	
_____ **17.** prairie pothole	**c.** Ridge formed at the edge of a glacier
_____ **18.** kettle	**d.** Shallow depression formed by flowing water
_____ **19.** cirque	**e.** Ridge at the farthest point reached by a glacier
_____ **20.** arête	**f.** Sharp ridge separating two cirques
_____ **21.** fiord	**g.** Bowl-shape hollow eroded by a glacier
	h. Sea-filled valley cut by a glacier in a coastal region

22. How were the Great Lakes formed? _____

    _____

    _____

    _____

© Prentice-Hall, Inc.

● ●

SECTION 8-5 **Waves and Wind**
(pages 280-285)

This section explains how waves form. The section also describes the erosion and deposition that waves and wind cause.

▶ How Waves Form (pages 280–281)

1. Circle the letter of each sentence that is true about the energy in waves.

   a. It comes from wind.

   b. It moves water particles up and down.

   c. It moves water particles forward.

   d. It moves across the water.

2. What part of the water is affected by a wave in deep water? _____

_____

_____

3. Circle the letter of each sentence that is true about a wave approaching land.

   a. It begins to drag on the bottom.

   b. It encounters more friction.

   c. It speeds up.

   d. It moves the water toward the land.

▶ Erosion by Waves (page 281)

4. Is the following sentence true or false? Waves are the major force of

   erosion along coasts. _____

5. List two ways that waves erode land.

   a. _____   **b.** _____

6. Part of the shore that sticks out into the ocean because it is made of

   harder rock is called a(n) _____.

© Prentice-Hall, Inc.

CHAPTER 8, Erosion and Deposition (continued)

▶ ## Landforms Created by Wave Erosion (page 282)

7. List three landforms created by wave erosion.

   a. _____ b. _____ c. _____

▶ ## Deposits by Waves (pages 282–283)

8. An area of wave-washed sediment along a coast is a(n)

   _____.

9. The process in which beach sediment is moved down the beach with

   the current is called _____.

10. How does a spit form? _____

   _____

   _____

11. How is a barrier beach formed? _____

   _____

   _____

12. Is the following sentence true or false? Storm winds can wash away

   barrier beaches. _____

▶ ## How Wind Causes Erosion (pages 283–284)

13. A deposit of wind-blown sand is a(n) _____.

14. Is the following sentence true or false? Wind alone is the strongest

   agent of erosion. _____

15. Why is wind very effective at causing erosion in deserts? _____

   _____

   _____

© Prentice-Hall, Inc.

4. Circle the letter of each sentence that is true about deflation.

   a. It is the main way wind causes erosion.

   b. It usually has a great effect on the land.

   c. It can create blowouts.

   d. It can create desert pavement.

5. Circle the letter of each sentence that is true about abrasion.

   a. It can polish rock.

   b. It is caused by wind-carried sand.

   c. It causes most desert landforms.

   d. It causes most erosion.

▶ Deposits Resulting From Wind Erosion (page 285)

6. Is the following sentence true or false? All the sediment picked up by wind eventually falls to the ground. _____

7. When does wind-carried sediment fall to the ground? _____

   _____

   _____

8. List two types of deposits formed by wind erosion and deposition.

   a. _____   b. _____

9. Complete the Venn diagram by adding the following phrases: have finer sediments, have coarser sediments, result from wind erosion.

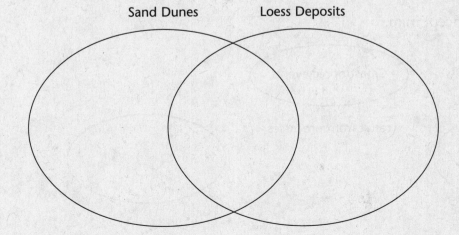

Sand Dunes   Loess Deposits

© Prentice-Hall, Inc.

CHAPTER 8, Erosion and Deposition *(continued)*

© Prentice-Hall, Inc.

SECTION 8-6	**Earth Systems and Catastrophic Events** (pages 286-290)

This section describes natural hazards and explains how human activities can increase the effects of natural hazards.

▶ Natural Hazards and Catastrophic Events (page 287)

1. What is a natural hazard? _____

_____

2. List six examples of natural hazards.

a. _____ b. _____ c. _____

d. _____ e. _____ f. _____

3. Is the following sentence true or false? Natural hazards care the result of

processes that take place in Earth systems. _____

4. Why are hurricanes and earthquakes natural hazards? _____

_____

_____

_____

▶ Impact on Earth (pages 288-289)

5. Compete the concept map.

Catastrophic events

result from processes

6. Describe two ways catastrophic events can change Earth's crust. _____

_____

_____

_____

▶ Human Activities (pages 289–290)

7. Is the following sentence true or false? Where people locate their activities can increase the damaging effects of natural hazards.

_____

8. Complete the flowchart to show how land use affects the impact of a natural hazard.

Forests on slopes hold soil in place and absorb _____.

↓

People clear forests for _____ and _____.

↓

Soil is not protected from _____.

↓

Hurricanes bring heavy _____.

↓

Runoff loosens the _____ and mud flows into river valleys.

9. Why is building a home on a flood plain risky? _____

_____

10. What is a tsunami? _____

_____

© Prentice-Hall, Inc.

CHAPTER 8, Erosion and Deposition (continued)

WordWise

Use the clues to help you unscramble the key terms from Chapter 8. Then put the numbered letters in the right order to spell out the answer to the riddle.

Clues	Key Terms

It's how sediment moves.   sorineo __ __ __ __ __ __ __
                                        1 2

It's how sediment settles.   oisontipde __ __ __ __ __ __ __ __ __ __
                                            3

It's a small particle that moves.   ideemtns __ __ __ __ __ __ __ __
                                                4   5

It's how much sediment a river carries.   adol __ __ __ __
                                                      6

It's the force that opposes motion   nfcotiri __ __ __ __ __ __ __ __
    of one surface across another.   7

It's how rocks are polished.   barinoas __ __ __ __ __ __ __ __
                                           8   9

It can be found where a river enters a lake.   ldtae __ __ __ __ __
                                                        10

It separates two drainage basins.   vdeiid __ __ __ __ __ __
                                              11

It's formed by a chunk of ice.   teketl __ __ __ __ __ __
                                           12

It sticks out in the water like a finger.   ipst __ __ __ __
                                                    13

It's a ridge at the edge of a glacier.   noamire __ __ __ __ __ __ __
                                                    14

It's a deposit of clay and silt.   seols __ __ __ __ __
                                           15

It's how most wind erosion occurs.   otefdalni __ __ __ __ __ __ __ __
                                                                 16

It flows into a larger stream.   tutyrabir __ __ __ __ __ __ __ __ __
                                             17   18

It's a kind of lake created by a river.   wxoob __ __ __ __ __
                                                   19

It's the ability to do work or cause change.   ynreeg __ __ __ __ __ __
                                                        20

Riddle: What shapes Earth's surface?

Answer: __ __ __ __ __ __ __ __ __ __ __ __ __ __ __ __ __ __ __ __
            1 2 3 4 5 6 7   8 9 10   11 12 13 14 15 16 17 18 19 20

© Prentice-Hall, Inc.

THE EARTH-MOON SYSTEM

· ·

SECTION 9–1 **Earth in Space** (pages 296-303)

This section explains what causes day and night and what causes the cycle of seasons on Earth.

▶ The Lengths of Days and Years (pages 297–299)

1. The study of the moon, stars, and other objects in space is called

_____.

Match the term with its definition.

Term	Definition
_____ 2. axis	**a.** The movement of one object around another object
_____ 3. rotation	**b.** The imaginary line that passes through Earth's center and the North and South poles
_____ 4. revolution	**c.** The path of an object as it revolves around another object in space
_____ 5. orbit	**d.** The spinning motion of a planet around its axis

6. Each 24-hour cycle of day and night is called a(n) _____.

7. Why is an extra day added to February every four years? _____

_____

_____

_____

_____

© Prentice-Hall, Inc.

CHAPTER 9, The Earth-Moon System (continued)

8. What causes day and night? _____

_____

▶ **Changes in Seasons** (pages 300–303)

9. Why is it warmer near the equator than near the poles? _____

_____

_____

_____

10. Why does Earth have seasons? _____

_____

_____

11. Circle the letter of each sentence that is true when the Northern Hemisphere has summer.

a. The Southern Hemisphere is tilted away from the sun.

b. The Northern Hemisphere is tilted away from the sun.

c. The Southern Hemisphere is tilted toward the sun.

d. The Northern Hemisphere is tilted toward the sun.

12. What is latitude? _____

_____

_____

13. Circle the letter of each sentence that is true about Earth's seasons.

a. Earth is closest to the sun when it is summer in the Northern Hemisphere.

b. The hemisphere that is tilted away from the sun has more daylight than the other hemisphere.

c. When it is summer in the Northern Hemisphere it is winter in the Southern Hemisphere.

d. In December, the sun's rays in the Northern Hemisphere are indirect.

© Prentice-Hall, Inc.

14. Each of the two days of the year when the sun is overhead at either 23.5° south or 23.5° north is called a(n) _____.

15. Each of the two days of the year when neither hemisphere is tilted toward or away from the sun is called a(n) _____.

16. Complete the table.

Earth's Seasons			
Day in Northern Hemisphere	Approximate Date Each Year	Length of Daytime	Which Hemisphere Is Tilted Toward the Sun?
Summer solstice			
Autumnal equinox			
Winter solstice			
Vernal equinox			

SECTION 9–2 **Phases, Eclipses, and Tides**
(pages 306-316)

This section explains what causes phases of the moon, what causes eclipses, and what causes the tides.

▶ **Introduction** (page 306)

1. What causes the phases of the moon, eclipses, and tides? _____

_____

▶ **The Moon's Orbit** (pages 306–307)

2. Circle the letter of each sentence that is true about motions of the moon.

a. The moon revolves around the Earth once a year.

b. The "near side" of the moon always faces Earth.

c. The moon rotates slowly on its axis once every 27.3 days.

d. The moon's orbit around Earth is an oval shape.

© Prentice-Hall, Inc.

CHAPTER 9, The Earth-Moon System (continued)

▶ Cyclical Phases of the Moon (pages 307–309)

3. The different shapes of the moon you see from Earth are called

   _____ .

4. How often does the moon go through a whole set of phases? _____

   _____

   _____

   _____

5. What does the phase of the moon you see depend on? _____

   _____

   _____

6. Complete the table about phases of the moon.

Phases of the Moon	
Phase	**What You See**
New moon	
First quarter	
Full moon	
Third quarter	

7. What causes the moon's phases? _____

   _____

   _____

8. Is the following sentence true or false? Half the moon is almost always in

   sunlight. _____

9. How long after the last new moon until a new moon occurs again?

   _____

© Prentice-Hall, Inc.

▶ Eclipses (page 309)

10. When the moon's shadow hits Earth or Earth's shadow hits the moon,

what occurs? _____

11. What are the two types of eclipses?

a. _____   b. _____

▶ Solar Eclipses (page 310)

12. What happens to cause a solar eclipse? _____

_____

_____

13. The darkest part of a shadow is called the _____.

14. The larger part of a shadow, surrounding the umbra, is called the

_____.

15. Circle the letter of each sentence that is true about solar eclipses.

   a. People in the umbra see only a partial solar eclipse.

   b. During a partial solar eclipse, part of the sun remains visible.

   c. During a total solar eclipse, the sky is dark.

   d. People in the penumbra see a total solar eclipse.

▶ Lunar Eclipses (page 311)

16. What is the arrangement of Earth, moon, and sun during a lunar

eclipse? _____

_____

17. Circle the letter of each sentence that is true about lunar eclipses.

   a. People in Earth's umbra see a total lunar eclipse.

   b. A lunar eclipse occurs at a full moon.

   c. During a lunar eclipse, Earth blocks sunlight from reaching the moon.

   d. A partial lunar eclipse occurs when the moon passes partly into the
   umbra of Earth's shadow.

© Prentice-Hall, Inc.

CHAPTER 9, The Earth-Moon System *(continued)*

▶ Tides *(page 314)*

18. The rise and fall of the level of the ocean are called _____.

19. What force pulls the moon and Earth toward each other?

_____

20. Why do tides occur? _____

_____

21. Circle the letter of each sentence that is true about tides.

    a. The point on Earth that is closest to the moon has a high tide.

    b. Every location on Earth has two high tides per month.

    c. A low tide occurs at the point on Earth farthest from the moon.

    d. The water left behind at the point on Earth farthest from the moon has a high tide.

22. What does the force of gravity between two objects depend on?

_____

23. Is the following sentence true or false? The sun has no influence on

Earth's tides. _____

24. What factors can make tides vary, even in places that are close to each

other? _____

_____

_____

 Reading Skill Practice

By looking carefully at illustrations in textbooks, you can help yourself understand better what you have read. Look carefully at Figure 6 on page 309. What important idea does this figure communicate?

© Prentice-Hall, Inc.

SECTION 9-3 Earth's Moon (pages 317-322)

This section describes the features of the moon that can be seen with a telescope. It also describes the missions to the moon.

▶ The Structure and Origin of the Moon (page 318)

1. Circle the letter of the approximate size of the moon.

   a. about twice the size of Earth

   b. about half Earth's diameter

   c. about the size of Hawaii

   d. about one quarter Earth's diameter

2. Complete the flowchart about the collision theory of the moon's origin.

A Theory of the Moon's Origin

A large object strikes _____.

↓

Material from _____ outer layer breaks off.

↓

The material from Earth is thrown into _____.

↓

Material in orbit forms the _____.

▶ Looking at the Moon From Earth (pages 318-319)

3. Who made a telescope in 1609 that allowed him to see details of the

   moon nobody had ever seen before? _____

   _____

© Prentice-Hall, Inc.

CHAPTER 9, The Earth-Moon System (continued)

4. Name three features on the moon's surface.

    a. _____

    b. _____

    c. _____

5. Round pits on the surface of the moon are called _____.

6. What are craters on the moon caused by? _____

_____

_____

7. Circle the letter of the phrase that best describes maria.

    a. Highland peaks that cast dark shadows

    b. Low, dry areas that were once flooded with molten material

    c. Vast oceans that cover much of the moon

    d. Craters made from exploded volcanoes

▶ Missions to the Moon (pages 320–322)

8. Which president of the United States launched an enormous program of space exploration and scientific research in the early 1960s?

_____

9. Circle the letter of the spacecraft that flew into orbit around the moon in July, 1969.

    a. *Surveyor*   **b.** *Sputnik 1*   **c.** *Skylab*   **d.** *Apollo 11*

10. Who was the first person to walk on the moon? _____

_____

11. What did Neil Armstrong say when he took his first step onto the moon?

_____

_____

© Prentice-Hall, Inc.

12. How have scientists learned about the material that makes up the

moon's surface? _____

_____

_____

13. How do scientists know that the moon's surface once was very hot?

_____

_____

_____

14. What did scientists conclude from moon rocks that had been broken

apart and then reformed? _____

_____

_____

15. Is the following sentence true or false? Seismometers detected extremely

strong moonquakes on the moon. _____

16. Is the following sentence true or false? The interior of the moon

remains very hot. _____

17. Circle the letter of each sentence that is true about the far side of the
moon.

a. It is almost completely covered with maria.

b. It is rougher than the near side.

c. It has few maria.

d. It is very smooth with no visible craters.

18. In 1998, what did the *Lunar Prospector* discover about the moon's poles?

_____

_____

_____

© Prentice-Hall, Inc.

CHAPTER 9, The Earth-Moon System *(continued)*

··

SECTION 9-4 **Is There Life Beyond Earth?**
(pages 323-326)

This section describes what conditions living things need to exist on Earth and explains why life might exist on Mars and Europa.

▶ **Introduction** (page 323)

1. Life other than that on Earth would be called

_____.

▶ **The "Goldilocks Conditions"** (pages 323–324)

2. What are the three "Goldilocks conditions" that Earth has that life as we know it needs to exist?

a. _____

b. _____

c. _____

3. On Earth, water exists as liquid, _____, and

_____.

▶ **Life on Earth** (page 324)

4. Where has life been found on Earth that suggests that life forms can

exist that do not need the "Goldilocks conditions"? _____

_____

_____

_____

_____

© Prentice-Hall, Inc.

▶ Life on Mars? (pages 325–326)

5. Why is Mars the most obvious place to look for living things like those

on Earth? _____

_____

6. Why do scientists hypothesize that Mars may once have had the

conditions needed for life to exist? _____

_____

_____

_____

7. A meteorite from Mars found in Antarctica in 1996 shows tiny shapes

that look like _____.

8. Is the following sentence true or false? All scientists agree that the
meteorite from Mars shows that life once existed on Mars.

_____

9. What tested the soil of Mars for signs of life? _____

_____

10. Is the following sentence true or false? Life has been discovered in

Martian soil. _____

▶ Life on Europa? (page 326)

11. What suggests that there might be liquid water on Europa? _____

_____

_____

_____

12. Is the following sentence true or false? If there is liquid water on Europa,

there might also be life. _____

© Prentice-Hall, Inc.

CHAPTER 9, The Earth-Moon System *(continued)*

WordWise

The hidden-word puzzle below contains 12 key terms from Chapter 9. You might find them across, down, or on the diagonal. Use the clues to identify the hidden terms. Then circle each term in the puzzle.

Clues	Key Terms
The spinning motion of a planet around its axis	_____
The study of the moon, stars, and other objects in space	_____
The shapes of the moon you see from Earth	_____
The imaginary line that passes through Earth's center and the North and South poles	_____
The two days of the year on which the sun is directly overhead at either 23.5° north or south	_____
Earth's path as it revolves around the sun	_____
The movement of one object around another object	_____
The rise or fall of the level of water in the ocean	_____
A round pit on the moon's surface	_____
The darkest part of a shadow	_____
Dark, flat areas on the moon's surface	_____
The part of a shadow that surrounds the darkest part	_____

```
x  c  r  a  t  e  r  r  u  q  r
p  a  s  t  r  o  n  o  m  y  e
e  x  o  m  o  n  t  t  b  w  v
n  i  l  m  a  r  i  a  r  l  o
u  s  s  d  e  n  b  t  a  t  l
m  w  t  d  c  m  s  i  m  i  u
b  s  i  k  p  m  b  o  t  a  t
r  t  c  m  l  s  s  n  p  t  i
a  a  e  u  i  l  k  a  i  d  o
y  p  h  a  s  e  s  h  n  u  n
```

© Prentice-Hall, Inc.

CHAPTER 10

BONES, MUSCLES, AND SKIN

SECTION 10-1 **Organization and Homeostasis** (pages 336-343)

This section tells how an animal's body is organized and describes the four types of tissue in animals. It also describes how the body maintains stable internal conditions.

▶ Levels of Organization (pages 336-337)

1. Is the following sentence true or false? Each part of an organism has a specific job to do, and all of the different parts work independently of

    each other. _____

2. List the levels of organization in organisms, starting with the smallest.

    a. _____ b. _____

    c. _____ d. _____

▶ Cells: Structure and Function (page 337)

3. The basic unit of structure and function in a living thing is a(n)

    _____.

4. Circle the letter of the outside boundary of an animal cell.

    a. cytoplasm   **b.** nucleus   **c.** tissue   **d.** cell membrane

5. The control center that directs the cell's activities and contains information that determines the cell's characteristics is the

    _____.

6. What is the cytoplasm? _____

    _____

    _____

© Prentice-Hall, Inc.

CHAPTER 10, Bones, Muscles, and Skin (continued)

7. Is the following sentence true or false? Cells carry on the processes that

keep organisms alive. _____

▶ Tissues (pages 338–339)

8. What is a tissue? _____

_____

9. Complete the table to show the functions and examples of the tissues in
the human body. See Figure 2 on page 338.

Tissues in the Human Body		
Tissue	**Function**	**Example**
Muscle		
Nerve		
Connective		
Epithelial		

▶ Organs and Organ Systems (page 339)

10. A structure that is made up of different kinds of tissues is a(n)

_____.

11. Circle the letter of the organ.

    a. muscle cell   **b.** blood   **c.** lungs   **d.** digestive system

12. What is an organ system? _____

_____

13. Organs in the circulatory system include the _____ and

_____.

© Prentice-Hall, Inc.

Match the organ system with its function. See Figure 3 on page 475.

Organ Systems	Functions
_____ 14. endocrine	a. Takes oxygen into the body
_____ 15. circulatory	b. Fights disease
_____ 16. excretory	c. Removes wastes
_____ 17. respiratory	d. Controls body process with chemicals
_____ 18. digestive	e. Takes food into the body and breaks it down
_____ 19. immune	f. Carries materials to and from body cells

▶ Maintaining Stable Internal Conditions (pages 340–341)

20. Is the following sentence true or false? The different body systems work

together and depend on one another. _____

21. The process by which an organism's internal environment is kept stable in

spite of changes in the external environment is called _____.

22. How do an animal's kidneys regulate water balance?

_____

_____

23. How do pores in the leaves of plants help control water balance?

_____

_____

24. How does perspiration help maintain constant body temperature?

_____

_____

25. An organism's _____ is the action or change in behavior
that occurs as a result of a stimulus.

26. Hunger is a(n) _____ stimulus.

© Prentice-Hall, Inc.

CHAPTER 10, Bones, Muscles, and Skin *(continued)*

▶ Stress and Homeostasis (pages 342–343)

27. What is stress? _____

_____

28. An event, such as an argument or an upcoming oral report, that causes

stress is a(n) _____.

29. Is the following sentence true or false? Stress does not affect homeostasis.

_____

30. What is adrenaline? _____

_____

_____

31. Complete the flowchart to show the effects of adrenaline on the body.

Adrenaline's Effects

Breathing _____, sending more oxygen to body cells to provide energy for the muscles.

↓

Extra oxygen gets to cells rapidly because the heart beats

_____.

↓

Arms and legs get _____ blood flowing to them.

The skin and digestive system get _____ blood.

↓

The pupils of the eyes get _____, so it is easier to see.

© Prentice-Hall, Inc.

32. What do the reactions of adrenaline prepare the body for? _____

_____

_____

▶ Long-Term Stress (page 343)

33. Is the following sentence true or false? The alarm stage of stress lasts for

a long time. _____

34. Is the following sentence true or false? Even if a stressful situation does

not go away, the body can still restore homeostasis. _____

35. What can happen to your body if you do not deal with stress? _____

_____

_____

36. Circle the letter of each sentence that is true about dealing with stress.

  a. It is important to ignore stressful situations so that they will go away.

  b. If you accept that you have a problem and deal with it, then your
  stress will decrease.

  c. You can avoid stress entirely.

  d. Talking to family members and friends about the stressful situation
  will help.

 Reading Skill Practice

A concept map is a useful tool to show the relationships between concepts. This helps make
the concepts easier to understand. Make a concept map to show the levels of organization in
complex organisms. For more information about concept maps, see page 660 in the Skills
Handbook of your textbook. Do your work on a separate sheet of paper.

© Prentice-Hall, Inc.

CHAPTER 10, Bones, Muscles, and Skin *(continued)*

SECTION 10–2 ## The Skeletal System
(pages 344-351)

This section describes the skeletal system and its function. It also tells how to keep your bones strong and healthy.

▶ **Functions of the Skeletal System** (pages 344–346)

1. List the five major functions of the skeleton.

   a. _____

   b. _____

   c. _____

   d. _____

   e. _____

2. Is the following sentence true or false? The structures of an organism's organs and organ systems are related to the functions they perform.

   _____

3. The 26 small bones that make up the backbone are the

   _____.

4. Is the following sentence true or false? Since the backbone is just one long

   bone, it allows your body to easily bend and twist. _____

5. How does the skeleton help the body move? _____

   _____

6. Circle the letter of the bone that protects the brain.

   a. backbone   **b.** pelvic girdle   **c.** ribs   **d.** skull

7. The long bones of the arms and legs make _____.

8. Calcium and phosphorus are _____ that are stored in bones.

© Prentice-Hall, Inc.

▶ Bones—Strong and Living (pages 346-347)

9. Circle the letter of each sentence that is true about bones.

   a. Bones are very strong and lightweight.

   b. Concrete can absorb more force without breaking than can bone.

   c. Bones make up over half of an adult's body weight.

   d. Bones are hard because they contain minerals.

10. When do bone cells form new bone tissue? _____

_____

_____

▶ The Structure of Bones (pages 347–348)

11. Label the parts of the bone in the diagram below.

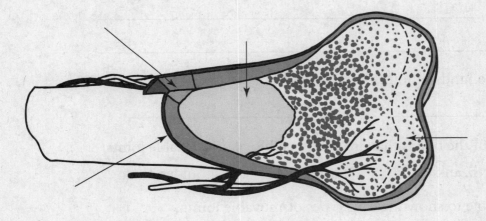

Match each part of a bone with its characteristics.

Bone Parts	Characteristics
_____ **12.** marrow	**a.** Where blood vessels and nerves enter and leave the bone
_____ **13.** outer membrane	**b.** Has small canals with blood vessels running through
_____ **14.** compact bone	**c.** Strong, but lightweight layer because it has many small spaces within it
_____ **15.** spongy bone	**d.** Soft connective tissue in the spaces in bone

© Prentice-Hall, Inc.

CHAPTER 10, Bones, Muscles, and Skin (continued)

▶ How Bones Form (page 348)

16. A connective tissue that is more flexible than bone is called

_____.

17. Circle the letter of each sentence that is true about how bones form.

   a. Much of an infant's skeleton is bone.

   b. As the body grows, the cartilage in the skeleton is replaced with hard bone tissue.

   c. By the time the body stops growing, all of the cartilage has been replaced with bone.

   d. Cartilage covers the ends of many bones in the body of an adult.

▶ Joints of the Skeleton (pages 348–350)

18. What is a joint? _____

_____

19. What are the two kinds of joints in the body?

   a. _____   b. _____

20. Circle the letter of the bones that are held together by immovable joints.

   a. knee   b. ankle   c. ribs   d. shoulder blade

21. Complete the table to show the four types of movable joints.

Movable Joints		
Joint	Kind of Motion	Where It's Found in the Body
Ball-and-socket		
Hinge		
Pivot		
Gliding		

© Prentice-Hall, Inc.

22. The bones in movable joints are held together by strong connective

tissues called _____.

▶ Taking Care of Your Bones (pages 350–351)

23. What can you do to keep your bones healthy? _____

_____

_____

24. A condition in which the body's bones become weak and break easily is

called _____.

 Reading Skill Practice

Photographs and illustrations help explain the ideas described in the reading. Look at Figure 10 on page 348. What idea is this photograph communicating? Do your work on a separate sheet of paper.

SECTION 10-3 The Muscular System (pages 352-356)

This section tells about the three kinds of muscle tissue in the human body, how muscles work to move the body, and how to care for your muscles.

▶ Muscle Action (page 352)

1. List the two groups of muscles in the body and describe how they are controlled.

a. _____

b. _____

2. Circle the letter of the action that is controlled by involuntary muscles.

a. smiling   **b.** breathing   **c.** walking   **d.** standing up

© Prentice-Hall, Inc.

CHAPTER 10, Bones, Muscles, and Skin (continued)

▶ Types of Muscles (pages 353–355)

3. Complete the table to compare and contrast the three types of muscle tissue in the body.

Types of Muscles			
Muscles	Location in Body	Voluntary or Involuntary	Striated or Not
Skeletal			
	Inside many internal organs		
Cardiac			

4. A strong connective tissue that attaches muscles to bone is a(n)

_____.

5. List two characteristics of skeletal muscles.

a. _____

b. _____

6. Is the following sentence true or false? Smooth muscles react more

quickly and tire more easily than skeletal muscles. _____

7. The repeated contractions of cardiac muscle are called

_____.

▶ Muscles at Work (page 355)

8. When do muscles contract, or become shorter and thicker? _____

_____

_____

9. Is the following sentence true or false? Muscle cells can extend, or get

longer, as well as contract, or get shorter. _____

© Prentice-Hall, Inc.

10. Why do skeletal muscles work in pairs to move a bone? _____

_____

_____

_____

11. To bend the elbow, the biceps muscle _____

and the triceps muscle returns to its _____.

▶ Taking Care of Your Skeletal Muscles (page 356)

12. Circle the letter of the sentence that is true about taking care of muscles.

   a. Exercise makes muscles thicker and stronger.

   b. Warming up muscles before exercise makes muscles more flexible.

   c. Muscles never get injured if you take proper care of them.

   d. Don't rest an injured muscle, it will heal on its own.

13. What causes a muscle strain, or pulled muscle? _____

_____

14. What happens when a muscle cramps? _____

_____

· ·

SECTION 10-4 The Skin (pages 358-364)

This section explains the structure of skin, what skin does, and how to keep skin healthy.

▶ The Body's Tough Covering (pages 358–359)

1. Circle the letter of each sentence that is true about the skin.

   a. The skin lets disease-causing microorganisms and harmful substances into the body.

   b. The skin keeps water from escaping from the body.

   c. The skin helps the body maintain homeostasis.

   d. The skin gathers information about the environment.

© Prentice-Hall, Inc.

CHAPTER 10, Bones, Muscles, and Skin (continued)

2. Is the following sentence true or false? To cool the body, blood vessels in the skin enlarge to let more blood run through them to move body heat to the outside. _____

3. Why are pain messages important to the body? _____

_____

_____

4. Skin cells produce _____ in the presence of sunlight.

▶ The Epidermis (pages 360–361)

5. The outermost layer of skin is the _____.

6. Is the following sentence true or false? Nerves and blood vessels run through the epidermis. _____

7. New cells that form deep in the epidermis gradually move upward to the surface of the skin, where after about _____, the cells die.

8. Is the following sentence true or false? The layer of dead cells on the surface of the skin gives the most protection to the body. _____

9. Is the following sentence true or false? Melanin, a pigment that gives skin its color, protects the skin from burning in sunlight. _____

▶ The Dermis (page 361)

10. The lower layer of the skin is the _____.

11. What is the role of the layer of fat below the dermis? _____

_____

_____

12. Circle the letter of each structure in the dermis.

a. hairs   b. bones   c. sweat glands   d. oil glands

© Prentice-Hall, Inc.

13. Perspiration reaches the surface of the skin through openings called

_____.

14. What are follicles? _____

_____

15. Is the following sentence true or false? Oil produced in glands around the hair follicles waterproofs the hair and keeps the skin moist.

_____

▶ **Caring for Your Skin** (pages 362–364)

16. Complete the concept map to show how to keep your skin healthy.

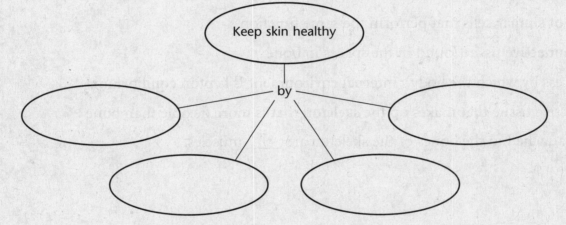

17. What should you do to replace the water that the skin loses during

perspiration? _____

_____

18. A disease in which some body cells divide uncontrollably is called

_____.

19. In what two ways does the sun damage your skin?

a. _____

b. _____

20. What is acne? _____

_____

© Prentice-Hall, Inc.

CHAPTER 10, Bones, Muscles, and Skin (continued)

WordWise

Use the clues below to identify key terms from Chapter 10. Write the terms on the line, putting one letter in each blank. When you finish, the word enclosed in the diagonal lines will reveal the name of the outermost layer of skin.

Clues

1. The basic unit of structure and function in a living thing

2. An opening in the dermis through which perspiration reaches the surface of the skin

3. A place in the body where two bones come together

4. A strong connective tissue that attaches muscle to bone

5. A group of similar cells that perform the same function

6. A soft connective tissue found in the spaces in bone

7. The process by which the body's internal environment is kept in equilibrium.

8. A connective tissue that makes up the skeleton that is more flexible than bone

9. Muscles attached to the bones of the skeleton are _____ muscles.

Key Terms

1. __ __ __ __
2. __ __ __ __
3. __ __ __ __ __
4. __ __ __ __ __ __
5. __ __ __ __ __ __
6. __ __ __ __ __
7. __ __ __ __ __ __ __ __ __ __
8. __ __ __ __ __ __ __
9. __ __ __ __ __ __ __ __ __

© Prentice-Hall, Inc.

CHAPTER 11

FOOD AND DIGESTION

. . . .

SECTION 11-1 **Food and Energy**
(pages 370-380)

This section tells about the six nutrients needed by the body. It also describes the Food Guide Pyramid and how to read labels on foods.

▶ Why You Need Food (pages 370–371)

1. What two things does food give to your body?

   a. _____

   b. _____

2. Is the following sentence true or false? Food is required for the body to

   maintain homeostasis, keeping a steady internal state. _____

3. The substances in food that give the raw materials and the energy

   needed by the body are called _____.

4. List the six kinds of nutrients that people need to stay healthy.

   a. _____ b. _____ c. _____

   d. _____ e. _____ f. _____

5. The amount of energy released by nutrients in the body is measured in

   units called _____.

6. Is the following sentence true or false? The more active you are, the more

   Calories you need. _____

▶ Carbohydrates (pages 371–372)

7. Carbohydrates are a major source of _____.

© Prentice-Hall, Inc.

CHAPTER 11, Food and Digestion (continued)

8. Is the following sentence true or false? Carbohydrates are not needed

for making new body cells. _____

Match the foods with the kinds of carbohydrates. Each kind of
carbohydrate may be used more than once.

Foods	Kinds of Carbohydrates
_____ **9.** fiber	**a.** Simple carbohydrate
_____ **10.** glucose	**b.** Complex carbohydrate
_____ **11.** starch	
_____ **12.** sugar	

▶ Fats (page 373)

13. What are fats? _____

_____

14. Circle the letter of the nutrient that provides the most energy.

    a. glucose   **b.** fats   **c.** carbohydrates   **d.** vitamins

15. List three jobs that fats have in the body.

    a. _____

    b. _____

    c. _____

16. Complete the following table to compare the two kinds of fats.

Kinds of Fats		
Characteristics	**Unsaturated Fats**	**Saturated Fats**
Liquid or Solid		
Foods Found In		

© Prentice-Hall, Inc.

17. Is the following sentence true or false? Cholesterol, a waxy, fatlike substance found only in animal products, is required in a balanced diet.

_____

18. Circle the letter of the maximum amount of your daily Calorie intake that should come from fats.

    a. 12 percent   **b.** 30 percent   **c.** 50 percent   **d.** 60 percent

▶ Proteins (page 374)

19. Nutrients that contain nitrogen, as well as carbon, hydrogen, and

    oxygen are called _____.

20. List three ways in which proteins are used by the body.

    a. _____

    b. _____

    c. _____

21. Is the following sentence true or false? The body can make all of the

    amino acids it needs to make proteins. _____

Match the kind of protein with its characteristics. Each kind of characteristic may be used more than once.

	Characteristics	Kinds of Proteins
_____	**22.** Missing one or more essential amino acids	**a.** complete protein
_____	**23.** Contains all the essential amino acids	**b.** incomplete protein
_____	**24.** Comes from animal sources, such as meat and eggs	
_____	**25.** Comes from plant sources, such as grains and nuts	

▶ Vitamins (pages 374–376)

26. What are vitamins? _____

    _____

    _____

© Prentice-Hall, Inc.

CHAPTER 11, Food and Digestion *(continued)*

27. Circle the letter of each sentence that is true about vitamins.

   a. The body needs large amounts of vitamins.

   b. Most people get the vitamins they need from foods.

   c. If you eat a variety of foods, you will get enough of each vitamin.

   d. Fat-soluble vitamins are stored in fatty tissues in the body.

▶ Minerals (page 376)

28. Nutrients that are not made by living things are called

_____.

29. How do you get minerals into your diet? _____

_____

Match the mineral with its function. See Figure 6 on page 512.

Minerals	Functions
_____ **30.** iron	**a.** Needed for normal muscle and nerve function
_____ **31.** fluorine	**b.** Helps maintain water balance
_____ **32.** magnesium	**c.** Forms an important part of red blood cells
_____ **33.** potassium	**d.** Helps form bones and teeth

▶ Water (page 377)

34. The most abundant substance in the body is _____.

35. Why is water the body's most important nutrient? _____

_____

_____

▶ The Food Guide Pyramid (pages 377–379)

36. How does the Food Guide Pyramid help you plan a healthy diet?

_____

_____

© Prentice-Hall, Inc.

37. Which foods in the pyramid should make up the largest part of the diet?

_____

_____

_____

38. The intake of foods in the _____ group should be limited.

▶ Food Labels (pages 379–380)

39. Is the following sentence true or false? All foods except meat, poultry, fresh vegetables, and fresh fruit must be labeled with nutrition

information. _____

40. How are food labels useful? _____

_____

41. The information on the food label, such as the number of Calories and

the nutrient content, is based on the _____.

42. What does it mean when a food label shows that Calories is equal to 110?

_____

_____

43. What is the Percent Daily Value on a food label? _____

_____

_____

44. The food label lists the ingredients in the food in order by

_____, starting with the main ingredient.

45. Why is it helpful to read the list of ingredients? _____

_____

_____

© Prentice-Hall, Inc.

CHAPTER 11, Food and Digestion *(continued)*

SECTION 11–2 **The Digestive Process Begins**
(pages 382-387)

This section explains what the digestive system does and describes the functions of the mouth, the throat, and the stomach.

▶ **Functions of the Digestive System** (pages 382–383)

1. Complete the flowchart to show the role of the digestive system.

Digestive System

The digestive system breaks down _____ into molecules the body can use.

↓

Then, molecules are absorbed into the _____ and carried throughout the body.

↓

Finally, the digestive system eliminates _____ from the body.

2. What is digestion? _____

_____

3. Is the following sentence true or false? In chemical digestion, foods are physically broken down into smaller pieces by chewing.

_____

4. The process by which nutrient molecules pass through the wall of the

digestive system and into the blood is called _____.

5. What happens to materials that are not absorbed? _____

_____

© Prentice-Hall, Inc.

▶ The Mouth (page 384)

6. The fluid released when your mouth waters is called _____.

7. Circle the letter of the object that begins the process of mechanical digestion in the mouth.

    a. saliva   **b.** teeth

    c. enzymes   **d.** mucus

8. What occurs during chemical digestion in the mouth? _____

_____

▶ The Esophagus (page 385)

Match each term with its definition.

	Terms	Definitions
_____	**9.** epiglottis	**a.** A thick, slippery substance that makes food easier to swallow
_____	**10.** esophagus	**b.** A flap of tissue that seals off the windpipe, preventing food from entering it
_____	**11.** mucus	**c.** A muscular tube that connects the mouth to the stomach
_____	**12.** peristalsis	**d.** Involuntary waves of muscle contraction that push food through the digestive system

13. _____ is a response that can remove harmful materials or disease-causing organisms from the body.

▶ The Stomach (pages 386–387)

14. Circle the letter of each sentence that is true about the stomach.

    a. The stomach is a J-shaped muscular pouch in the abdomen.

    b. Mechanical digestion does not occur in the stomach.

    c. Digestive juice in the stomach contains an enzyme that breaks down proteins.

    d. Hydrochloric acid in the stomach kills many bacteria that are swallowed with food.

© Prentice-Hall, Inc.

CHAPTER 11, Food and Digestion (continued)

15. Give two reasons why the hydrochloric acid in the digestive juice does not damage the stomach.

a. _____

b. _____

 Reading Skill Practice

Using the glossary is a quick way to look up the meanings of key terms in the textbook. The glossary is located in the back of your textbook, beginning on page 681. Make a list of the key terms in this section. Then use the glossary to write the definition for each. Do your work on a separate sheet of paper.

SECTION 11–3 **Final Digestion and Absorption**
(pages 390–393)

This section describes the functions of the small and large intestines in digestion.

▶ **The Small Intestine** (pages 390–392)

1. What takes place in the small intestine? _____

_____

2. List the three organs that produce the enzymes and secretions used in the small intestine.

a. _____ b. _____ c. _____

3. The largest and heaviest organ inside the body that is located in the

upper part of the abdomen is the _____.

4. The liver produces a substance called _____, which breaks up fat particles.

© Prentice-Hall, Inc.

5. Enzymes produced by the pancreas help break down

_____, _____, and _____.

6. What is the role of fiber? _____

_____

_____

7. The tiny finger-shaped structures that cover the inner surface of the

small intestine are called _____.

8. Is the following sentence true or false? Nutrient molecules pass from
the small intestine into the bloodstream through the villi.

_____

▶ **The Large Intestine** (page 393)

9. Is the following sentence true or false? The bacteria in the large
intestine feed on the material passing through and make certain

vitamins for the body. _____

10. Complete the concept map to show the role of the large intestine.

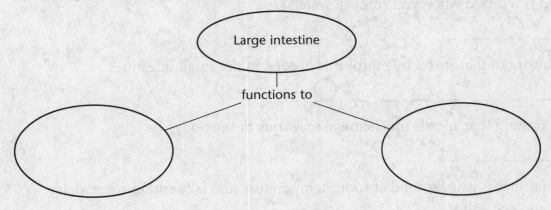

11. The short tube at the end of the large intestine where waste material is

compressed is called the _____.

12. Circle the letter of the muscular opening through which wastes are
removed from the body.

   a. rectum   **b.** anus   **c.** pancreas   **d.** villi

© Prentice-Hall, Inc.

CHAPTER 11, Food and Digestion (continued)

WordWise

Answer the questions by writing the correct key term in the blanks. Use the circled letter in each term to find the hidden key term. Then write a definition for the hidden key term.

1. What is the triangular organ that lies between the stomach and the first part of the small intestine and produces enzymes that help break down starches, proteins, and fats?

   _ _ Ⓞ _ _ _ _ _

2. What is a thick, slippery substance produced by the body that makes food move more easily through the digestive system?

   _ _ _ Ⓞ _

3. What nutrient acts as a helper molecule in many different chemical reactions within the body?

   _ _ Ⓞ _ _ _ _ _

4. What is the process by which nutrient molecules pass through the wall of the digestive system into the blood?

   _ _ _ _ Ⓞ _ _ _ _ _

5. What fluid is released when your mouth waters?

   _ _ _ Ⓞ _ _

6. What is the organ that stores bile until it is needed in the small intestine?

   _ _ _ _ _ _ _ _ _ Ⓞ _

7. What is a protein that speeds up chemical reactions in the body?

   _ Ⓞ _ _ _ _ _

8. What is a fat that is usually solid at room temperature and is found in meat, dairy products, and egg yolks?

   _ _ Ⓞ _ _ _ _ _ _ _ _ _ _

Key Term: _ _ _ _ _ _ _ _

Definition: _____

_____

© Prentice-Hall, Inc.

CHAPTER 12

CIRCULATION

••

SECTION 12-1 The Body's Transportation System
(pages 400-406)

This section describes how the heart, blood vessels, and blood work together to carry materials throughout the body.

▶ Movement of Materials (pages 400–401)

1. Another name for the cardiovascular system is the _____ system.

2. Complete this concept map to show what makes up the cardiovascular system.

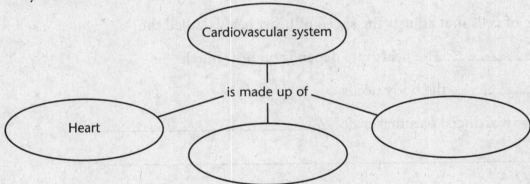

3. What three things are carried throughout the body by the cardiovascular

   system? _____

   _____

▶ Structure and Function of the Heart (pages 402–403)

4. Each time the heart beats, what does it do to blood? _____

   _____

   _____

© Prentice-Hall, Inc.

CHAPTER 12, Circulation (continued)

5. Complete the table about the chambers of the heart.

Chambers of the Heart		
Questions	Upper Chambers	Lower Chambers
What are these chambers called?		
How many are there?		
What is the function, or job, of these chambers?		

6. A flap of tissue that prevents blood from flowing backward is a(n)

_____.

▶ Regulation of Heartbeat (page 404)

7. The group of cells that adjusts the speed of heart beat is called the

_____. The heart rate depends on how much

_____ the body needs.

8. What does an artificial pacemaker do? _____

_____

▶ Two Loops (pages 404–406)

9. Name the three kinds of blood vessels. _____

_____

10. Describe the loop in which the blood picks up oxygen. _____

_____

_____

_____

© Prentice-Hall, Inc.

11. Draw arrows on the diagram at the right to show how blood circulates through the body. The first arrow should start in the right ventricle.

12. The largest artery in the body is call

the _____.

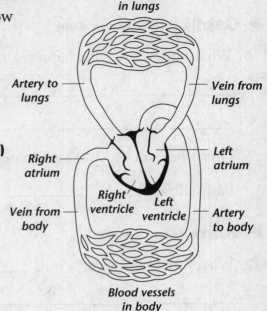

Blood vessels in lungs

Artery to lungs — **Vein from lungs**

Right atrium — **Left atrium**

Right ventricle — **Left ventricle**

Vein from body — **Artery to body**

Blood vessels in body

▶ The Force of the Ventricles (page 406)

13. What causes the force that pushes blood

throughout your body? _____

_____

_____

- -

SECTION 12–2 A Closer Look at Blood Vessels
(pages 407–411)

This section describes three kinds of blood vessels that are found in your body.

▶ Arteries (pages 407–409)

1. Arteries carry blood away from the _____.

2. Is the following sentence true or false? The coronary arteries provide

the stomach with its blood supply. _____

3. Circle the letter of each sentence that is true about pulse.

    a. The faster your heart beats, the slower your pulse will be.

    b. Pulse is caused by the expanding and narrowing of artery walls.

    c. When you count pulse beats, you are also counting heartbeats.

    d. You can feel pulse in veins but not in arteries.

4. Is the following sentence true or false? Arteries control the amount of

blood that different organs receive. _____

© Prentice-Hall, Inc.

CHAPTER 12, Circulation *(continued)*

▶ Capillaries (page 409)

5. What important thing happens in the capillaries? _____

_____

_____

6. One process in which materials are exchanged between the blood and the

body cells is _____.

▶ Veins (page 410)

7. What job do veins carry out? _____

_____

8. What three things help push blood through veins?

a. _____

b. _____

c. _____

▶ Blood Pressure (pages 410–411)

9. What is blood pressure? _____

_____

10. Is the following sentence true or false? Blood flowing through arteries exerts

the highest pressure. _____

 Reading Skill Practice

By looking carefully at photographs and illustrations in textbooks, you can help yourself
understand what you have read. Look carefully at Figure 9 on page 410. What important idea
does this photograph communicate?

© Prentice-Hall, Inc.

SECTION 12-3 Blood and Lymph (pages 413-418)

This section explains what blood is made of and describes the jobs performed by the different parts of blood. This section also describes the lymphatic system.

▶ Introduction (page 413)

1. What is the name for the liquid part of blood? _____

2. Complete the concept map below by naming the types of cells that are found in blood.

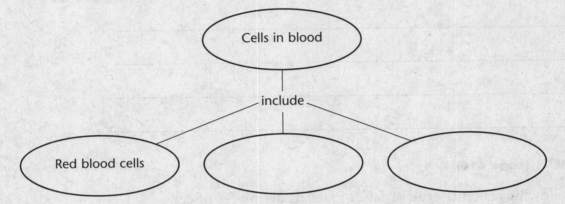

▶ Plasma (page 413)

3. What is plasma mostly made up of? _____

4. List four kinds of materials that are carried in plasma.

    a. _____

    b. _____

    c. _____

    d. _____

▶ Red Blood Cells (pages 414–415)

5. What job do red blood cells perform in the body? _____

_____

_____

© Prentice-Hall, Inc.

CHAPTER 12, Circulation *(continued)*

6. What is hemoglobin, and where is it found? _____

_____

_____

_____

▶ White Blood Cells (page 415)

7. What is the job of white blood cells? _____

8. List four ways in which white blood cells are different from red blood cells.

a. _____

b. _____

c. _____

d. _____

▶ Platelets (page 416)

9. Is the following sentence true or false? Platelets are pieces of cells.

_____

10. Describe how a blood clot forms. _____

_____

_____

▶ Blood Types (pages 416–417)

Match the blood type with the kinds of clumping proteins in its plasma.

Blood Type	Clumping Proteins in Its Plasma
_____ 11. A	**a.** no clumping proteins
_____ 12. B	**b.** anti-B proteins
_____ 13. AB	**c.** both anti-A and anti-B proteins
_____ 14. O	**d.** anti-A proteins

© Prentice-Hall, Inc.

15. What is a blood transfusion? _____

_____

16. Why can't a person with blood type A safely receive a transfusion of

blood type B? _____

_____

_____

▶ The Lymphatic System (page 418)

17. What is the lymphatic system? _____

_____

_____

18. The fluid inside the lymphatic system is called _____.

19. How do lymph nodes help fight disease? _____

_____

_____

SECTION 12–4	# Cardiovascular Health (pages 420–424)

This section describes diseases of the cardiovascular system. The section also identifies steps that people can take to help prevent these diseases.

▶ Cardiovascular Disease (page 421)

1. What is atherosclerosis? _____

_____

_____

2. What is cholesterol? _____

_____

© Prentice-Hall, Inc.

CHAPTER 12, Circulation (continued)

3. Complete the flowchart below, which describes what can happen when atherosclerosis develops in the coronary arteries.

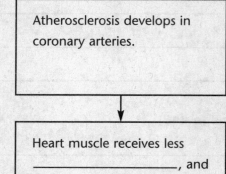

Atherosclerosis develops in coronary arteries.

Heart muscle receives less _____, and therefore its cells receive less _____.

A(n) _____ occurs, which means that blood flow to part of the heart is blocked.

▶ Hypertension (pages 421–423)

4. What is hypertension? _____

_____

_____

5. Give two reasons why hypertension is a serious problem. _____

_____

_____

_____

6. What is done to treat hypertension? _____

_____

_____

© Prentice-Hall, Inc.

▶ **Keeping Your Cardiovascular System Healthy** (page 424)

7. To help maintain cardiovascular health, people should eat a diet that is low in these substances.

a. _____

b. _____

c. _____

8. Is the following sentence true or false? Even if smokers quit, they cannot

decrease their risk of death from cardiovascular disease. _____

9. In the table below, explain why each behavior is important for cardiovascular health.

Cardiovascular Health	
Behavior	**Why It Is Important**
Getting a lot of exercise	
Eating healthy foods	
Not smoking	

 Reading Skill Practice

Outlining is a way to help yourself understand and remember what you have read. Write an outline of this section on cardiovascular health. In an outline, copy the headings in the textbook. Under each heading, write the main idea of that part of the lesson. Then list the details that support that main idea.

© Prentice-Hall, Inc.

CHAPTER 12, Circulation *(continued)*

Word Wise

See how fast you can solve this crossword puzzle. You'll need to use what you've learned about the cardiovascular system. Go!

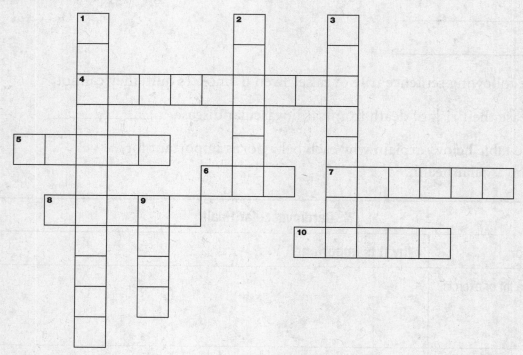

Clues down

1. Tiny blood vessels in which substances are exchanged between the blood and body cells
2. The liquid part of blood
3. The kind of artery that supplies blood to the heart itself
9. A blood vessel that carries blood back to the heart

Clues across

4. A group of cells located in the right atrium that regulates heartbeat rate
5. The alternating expansion and contraction of artery walls caused by the contraction and relaxation of the ventricles; can be felt if you touch your wrist
6. To keep your heart healthy, you should limit this in the food you eat.
7. A chamber of the heart that receives blood that comes into the heart
8. A flap of tissue that prevents blood from flowing backward
10. The fluid that the lymphatic system collects and returns to the bloodstream

© Prentice-Hall, Inc.

CHAPTER 13

RESPIRATION AND EXCRETION

SECTION 13-1 **The Respiratory System**
(pages 430-438)

This section describes the parts of the respiratory system and how they work to help you breathe and speak.

▶ **Introduction** (page 430)

1. What are two functions of the respiratory system?

   a. _____

   b. _____

▶ **Why the Body Needs Oxygen** (pages 430–431)

2. The chemical reactions to release energy that take place inside your cells

   must have _____.

3. What is respiration? _____

   _____

   _____

4. List three products of respiration.

   a. _____   b. _____   c. _____

5. Is the following sentence true or false? To a scientist, *breathing* and

   respiration mean the same thing. _____

6. Circle the letter of each organ system that the respiratory system depends on.

   a. circulatory system   **b.** reproductive system

   c. excretory system   **d.** digestive system

© Prentice-Hall, Inc.

CHAPTER 13, Respiration and Excretion *(continued)*

▶ The Air You Breathe (page 431)

7. Circle the letter of each sentence that is true about oxygen.

   a. The air you breathe is part of the atmosphere, the blanket of gases that surrounds Earth.

   b. Oxygen makes up about 78 percent of the gases in the atmosphere.

   c. Your body uses all of the air that you breathe into your lungs.

   d. Most of the air you breathe in goes back into the atmosphere when you exhale.

▶ The Path of Air (pages 432–434)

8. Is the following sentence true or false? When you breathe in air, you

   also breathe in dust, pollen, and microorganisms. _____

9. Complete the flowchart to show the path of air as it travels to the lungs.

The Path of Air

Air enters the body through two _____, or openings, in the nose.

↓

Air moves through the _____, which is also a part of the digestive system.

↓

Air moves into the _____, or windpipe.

↓

Air moves through the _____, passages that direct air into the lungs.

10. What does a sneeze do? _____

_____

11. Another name for the pharynx is the _____.

© Prentice-Hall, Inc.

Match the parts of the nose with their functions.

Parts	Functions
_____ 12. nostrils	**a.** Moistens the air and traps particles in the air
_____ 13. nasal cavities	**b.** Openings in the nose through which air enters
_____ 14. mucus	**c.** Tiny hairlike extensions that sweep mucus into the throat
_____ 15. cilia	**d.** Contain blood vessels that heat the air you breathe in

16. Circle the letter of each body part that is connected to the pharynx.

    a. stomach   **b.** nose   **c.** mouth   **d.** ears

17. The walls of the trachea are made up of rings of _____ that strengthen the trachea and keep it open.

18. Is the following sentence true or false? The cilia and mucus in the trachea sweep upward, moving the mucus toward the nose where it is

    sneezed out. _____

19. If food enters the trachea, a person can _____.

20. Circle the letter of the main organs of the respiratory system.

    a. trachea   **b.** bronchi   **c.** lungs   **d.** alveoli

21. Is the following sentence true or false? Inside the lungs, each bronchus

    divides into smaller and smaller tubes. _____

22. What happens in the alveoli? _____

    _____

▶ Structure and Function in Gas Exchange (page 435)

23. What occurs during the process of gas exchange? _____

    _____

    _____

© Prentice-Hall, Inc.

CHAPTER 13, Respiration and Excretion (continued)

24. Why can the lungs absorb a large amount of oxygen? _____

_____

_____

▶ How You Breathe (pages 436–437)

25. Is the following sentence true or false? The more oxygen you need, the

more slowly you breathe. _____

26. What is the diaphragm? _____

_____

27. Complete the cycle diagram to show the process of breathing.

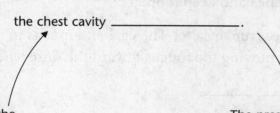

Rib muscles and diaphragm contract, making

the chest cavity _____.

The air is squeezed out of the

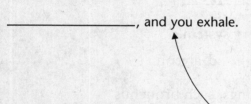

_____, and you exhale.

The pressure of the air inside the lungs

_____.

The rib muscles and diaphragm relax, and the

chest cavity becomes _____.

Air rushes into the lungs, and you

_____.

▶ How You Speak (pages 437–438)

28. Another name for the voice box is the _____.

29. What are vocal cords? _____

_____

_____

© Prentice-Hall, Inc.

30. How do vocal cords create your voice? _____

_____

_____

_____

📖 Reading Skill Practice

Taking notes while you read is a very helpful way to remember what you have read. To take notes, write down the headings in the section. Under each heading, write the main idea and important details that you read about. You should also include the key terms and their definitions in your notes. Reread this section. As you read, take notes about what you are reading. Do your work on a separate sheet of paper.

• •

SECTION 13–2 **Smoking and Your Health**
(pages 440–444)

This section explains what harmful chemicals are in tobacco smoke and how these chemicals harm the body.

▶ Chemicals in Tobacco Smoke (pages 440–441)

1. Complete the table to show the harmful chemicals in tobacco smoke.

Harmful Chemicals in Tobacco Smoke		
Chemical	**What It Is**	**How It Harms the Body**
Tar		
Carbon monoxide		
	A drug that produces an addiction, or physical dependence	

© Prentice-Hall, Inc.

CHAPTER 13, Respiration and Excretion *(continued)*

▶ Respiratory System Problems (pages 441–442)

2. Circle the letter of each sentence that is true about the effects of tobacco smoke.

    a. Tobacco smoke does not harm the respiratory system.

    b. Smokers cough frequently because their cilia cannot sweep away mucus.

    c. Smokers do not get as much oxygen because mucus buildup blocks air flow into the lungs.

    d. Heavy smokers can easily take part in vigorous sports.

3. List three respiratory problems that result from long-term smoking.

    a. _____   **b.** _____   **c.** _____

4. Is the following sentence true or false? Long-term bronchitis has no

effect on the breathing passages. _____

5. A serious disease that destroys lung tissue and causes difficulty in

breathing is _____.

6. What causes emphysema? _____

_____

_____

7. Is the following sentence true or false? Cigarette smoke has over 40

different chemicals that cause cancer. _____

▶ Circulatory System Problems (page 443)

8. How do the chemicals in tobacco smoke affect blood vessels?

_____

_____

_____

_____

© Prentice-Hall, Inc.

9. Is the following sentence true or false? Smokers are more likely to have

heart attacks than nonsmokers. _____

▶ Passive Smoking (page 443)

10. What is passive smoking? _____

_____

_____

11. Is the following sentence true or false? Passive smoking causes
respiratory problems and increases the risk of heart disease and lung

cancer in nonsmokers. _____

▶ Choosing Not to Smoke (page 444)

12. Most smokers began smoking when they were _____.

13. List two reasons why people are tempted to start smoking.

a. _____

b. _____

14. Is the following sentence true or false? It is very easy to stop smoking

once you have started. _____

- -

SECTION 13-3 The Excretory System (pages 445-450)

This section explains how the parts of the excretory system work.

▶ Introduction (page 445)

1. What is the function of the excretory system? _____

_____

_____

_____

© Prentice-Hall, Inc.

CHAPTER 13, Respiration and Excretion (continued)

2. The process of removing wastes from the body is _____.

▶ The Organs of the Excretory System (pages 445–446)

3. What are three wastes that the body must get rid of? _____

_____

Match the term with its definition.

Terms	Definitions
_____ 4. urea	a. The major organs of the excretory system
_____ 5. kidneys	b. A watery fluid produced by the kidneys
_____ 6. urine	c. A chemical that comes from the breakdown of proteins

7. Complete the flowchart to show how wastes are removed from the body.

Removing Wastes

Blood flows through the kidneys.

Kidneys filter the _____, removing the wastes.

Urine flows from the kidneys through two narrow tubes called _____

to a sacklike muscular organ called the _____, which stores urine.

When the bladder is full, urine flows out of the body through a tube called the

_____.

▶ The Filtering Process (pages 446–448)

8. What are nephrons? _____

_____

_____

© Prentice-Hall, Inc.

9. What are the stages of urine formation?

a. _____

b. _____

10. Is the following sentence true or false? Urea and glucose stay in the capillaries while blood cells and protein molecules move into the

capsule of a nephron. _____

11. List the substances that are returned to the blood and those that stay in the kidneys after the kidneys filter the blood.

Returned to blood: _____

Stay in kidneys: _____

12. Why is a chemical analysis of urine useful to doctors? _____

_____

_____

_____

▶ Water Balance in the Body (pages 449–450)

13. The kidneys help maintain homeostasis by regulating the amount of

_____ in the body.

14. Is the following sentence true or false? If you've been sweating a lot and haven't had much to drink, your body will absorb less water and

produce a larger volume of urine. _____

▶ Other Organs of Excretion (page 450)

15. What are three other organs of excretion, not including the kidneys?

a. _____   b. _____   c. _____

16. What is the function of the liver? _____

_____

_____

© Prentice-Hall, Inc.

CHAPTER 13, Respiration and Excretion (continued)

WordWise

Use the clues to help you unscramble the key terms from Chapter 13. Then put the numbered letters in order to find the answer to the riddle.

Clues	Key Terms
It's the result of proteins breaking down.	euar __ __ __ __ 1
It's tiny sacs of lung tissue.	vlelioa __ __ __ __ __ __ __ 2
It's an irritation of the breathing passages.	crtoibnsih __ __ __ __ __ __ __ __ __ __ 3
It's a tiny filtering factory in the kidneys.	renhnop __ __ __ __ __ __ __ 4
It's a large muscle that helps you breathe.	gahmdairp __ __ __ __ __ __ __ __ __ 5
It's a small tube through which urine leaves the body.	reahrut __ __ __ __ __ __ __ 6
It's the voice box.	yranxl __ __ __ __ __ __ 7
It's a dark substance and makes cilia clump together.	rta __ __ __ 8
They're tiny, hairlike, and sweep mucus around.	alici __ __ __ __ __ 9
It's a dangerous chemical in tobacco smoke.	tnocinei __ __ __ __ __ __ __ __ 10
It's the major organ of the excretory system.	ydnkie __ __ __ __ __ __ 11

Riddle: What process releases energy from oxygen and glucose?

Answer: __ __ __ __ __ __ __ __ __ __ __
          1 2 3 4 5 6 7 8 9 10 11

© Prentice-Hall, Inc.

CHAPTER 14

FIGHTING DISEASE

....

SECTION 14-1 Infectious Disease (pages 456-457)

This section explains how infectious diseases are caused and what kinds of organisms cause disease.

▶ Disease and Pathogens (page 457)

1. Organisms that cause disease are called _____.

2. What is an infectious disease? _____

_____

_____

3. Is the following sentence true or false? Pathogens make you sick by

damaging individual cells. _____

4. Complete the concept map to show the different kinds of pathogens.

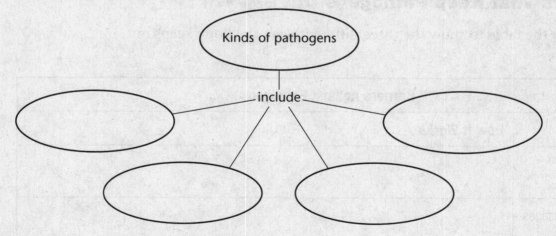

5. Circle the letter of the kind of pathogen that causes malaria.

    a. bacteria   **b.** viruses   **c.** fungi   **d.** protists

© Prentice-Hall, Inc.

CHAPTER 14, Fighting Disease *(continued)*

6. Louis Pasteur's work led to the process of _____,
   in which heat is used to kill microorganisms.

▶ **How Diseases Are Spread** (pages 458–459)

7. List four sources of pathogens.

   a. _____   b. _____

   c. _____   d. _____

8. Circle each sentence that is true about how diseases are spread.

   a. People cannot get pathogens by drinking water.

   b. People can get pathogens by using a towel that was handled by an
      infected person.

   c. Animals cannot spread pathogens to people.

   d. Some pathogens live in soil or water.

· ·

SECTION 14–2 **The Body's Defenses**
(pages 460–468)

This section describes how the body protects itself from pathogens.

▶ **Barriers That Keep Pathogens Out** (page 461)

1. Complete the table to show the three different ways the body keeps out
   pathogens.

Barriers Against Pathogens	
Barrier	**How It Works**
Skin	
Breathing passages	
Mouth and stomach	

Science Explorer Grade 7

© Prentice-Hall, Inc.

2. What is the body's first line of defense against pathogens? _____

_____

_____

_____

▶ General Defenses (page 464)

3. The second line of defense in the body is the _____

_____, which occurs when body cells are damaged.

4. What happens in the inflammatory response? _____

_____

_____

_____

5. The kinds of white blood cells that take part in the inflammatory

response are called _____, which engulf pathogens and
destroy them.

6. Why is the affected area red and swollen during the inflammatory

response? _____

_____

7. How does a fever help your body? _____

_____

_____

▶ Function of the Immune System (pages 465–466)

8. The third line of defense against pathogens in the body is the

_____.

9. List the two major kinds of lymphocytes.

a. _____   b. _____

© Prentice-Hall, Inc.

CHAPTER 14, Fighting Disease (continued)

10. Complete the flowchart to show what occurs during the immune response.

Immune Response

A(n) _____ recognizes a pathogen.

Some _____ attack and kill infected cells and the

pathogen. Others alert _____ to produce antibodies.

The pathogens are destroyed by _____ that bind to
the antigens on the pathogens.

11. What can lymphocytes do? _____

_____

_____

12. What are antigens? _____

_____

_____

13. List three ways that antibodies help destroy pathogens.

a. _____

b. _____

c. _____

▶ AIDS, a Disease of the Immune System (pages 467–468)

14. What causes acquired immunodeficiency syndrome, or AIDS?

_____

_____

© Prentice-Hall, Inc.

15. Once HIV enters the body, it enters _____ and reproduces inside them.

16. Is the following sentence true or false? Over time, HIV damages the immune system, and the body loses its ability to fight disease.

_____

17. Circle the letter of each sentence that is true about how HIV is spread.

   a. HIV may spread from an infected woman to her baby through breast milk.

   b. HIV is not spread by sexual contact.

   c. HIV is spread by shaking hands.

   d. HIV is not spread by using a toilet seat after it has been used by someone with HIV.

. . . .

SECTION 14–3 Preventing Infectious Disease
(pages 469–473)

This section describes two different kinds of immunity and some ways to stay healthy.

▶ Introduction (page 469)

1. The body's ability to destroy pathogens before they can cause disease is

called _____.

2. What are the two types of immunity?

   a. _____   b. _____

▶ Active Immunity (pages 469–472)

3. When does active immunity occur? _____

_____

_____

4. Is the following sentence true or false? Activity immunity is produced by the cells of the immune system as part of the immune response.

_____

© Prentice-Hall, Inc.

CHAPTER 14, Fighting Disease *(continued)*

5. How do memory cells keep a person from getting sick? _____

_____

_____

6. The process by which harmless antigens are introduced into a person's

body to produce active immunity is called _____, or
immunization.

7. What does a vaccine consist of? _____

_____

_____

_____

▶ Passive Immunity (page 472)

8. When antibodies are given to a person and are not made by the person's

immune system, the person is protected by _____
immunity.

9. Is the following sentence true or false? Passive immunity can last a

lifetime. _____

10. How does a baby get passive immunity? _____

_____

_____

▶ Staying Healthy (page 473)

11. Circle the letter of each action that helps prevent infectious diseases.

a. Share toothbrushes and silverware.

b. Wash hands before eating and after using the bathroom.

c. Cover your mouth when sneezing or coughing.

d. Stay up late every night.

© Prentice-Hall, Inc.

12. What three things can you do to help your body recover when you are sick?

a. _____

b. _____

c. _____

13. A chemical that kills bacteria or slows their growth without harming

body cells is a(n) _____.

14. Is the following sentence true or false? Some medicines don't kill pathogens, but help you to feel more comfortable while you get better.

_____

Reading Skill Practice

Venn diagrams compare and contrast the features of two different things. Make a Venn diagram to show the similarities and differences between active immunity and passive immunity. For more information about Venn diagrams, see page 661 in the Skills Handbook of your textbook. Do your work on a separate sheet of paper.

SECTION 14-4 Noninfectious Disease (pages 476-480)

This section describes three different diseases that are not spread from person to person.

▶ Introduction (page 476)

1. Diseases that are not spread from person to person are called

_____ diseases.

2. Is the following sentence true or false? Over the years, infectious diseases

have grown more prevalent. _____

© Prentice-Hall, Inc.

CHAPTER 14, Fighting Disease *(continued)*

▶ Allergies (pages 476–477)

3. What is an allergy? _____

_____

4. Any substance that causes an allergy is a(n) _____.

5. Circle the letter of each item that people may be allergic to.

   a. pollen   **b.** some foods   **c.** some medicines   **d.** molds

6. Antibodies produced during the allergy response signal the body to

   release _____, a chemical that causes sneezing and
   watery eyes.

7. Is the following sentence true or false? If you have an allergy, the best
   thing to do is avoid the substance to which you are allergic.

   _____

8. What is asthma? _____

_____

▶ Diabetes (page 478)

9. Circle the letter of the chemical that enables body cells to take in
   glucose from the blood and use it for energy.

   a. diabetes   **b.** allergen   **c.** insulin   **d.** histamine

10. The pancreas fails to produce enough insulin or the body cells aren't

    using glucose properly in _____.

11. Is the following sentence true or false? A person with diabetes has low
    levels of glucose in the blood and more than enough glucose in the

    body cells. _____

12. Circle the letter of each effect of diabetes.

    a. Never feel hungry   **b.** Lose weight

    c. Feel thirsty   **d.** Rarely urinate.

© Prentice-Hall, Inc.

13. Complete the table to compare the two types of diabetes.

Forms of Diabetes		
Questions	**Type I**	**Type II**
When does it begin?		
What is wrong?		
How is it treated?		

▶ Cancer (pages 478–480)

14. What is cancer? _____

_____

_____

15. As cancerous cells divide over and over, they form abnormal tissue

masses called _____.

16. What are two causes of cancer?

    a. _____

    b. _____

17. Is the following sentence true or false? Surgery, drugs, and radiation are

all used to treat cancer. _____

18. Circle the letter of each sentence that is true about preventing cancer.

    a. Avoid tobacco.

    b. Expose your skin to sunlight frequently.

    c. Eat plenty of fatty foods.

    d. Visit the doctor regularly for medical checkups.

© Prentice-Hall, Inc.

CHAPTER 14, Fighting Disease (continued)

WordWise

Match each definition on the left with the correct term on the right. Then write the number of each term in the appropriate box below. When you have filled in all the boxes, add up the numbers in each column, row, and two diagonals. The sums should be the same. Some terms may not be used.

A. A chemical that kills bacteria or slows their growth without harming body cells

B. Consists of pathogens that have been weakened or killed but can trigger the immune system

C. The body's ability to destroy pathogens before they can cause disease

D. A chemical that destroys a pathogen by locking onto its antigen

E. A lymphocyte that identifies pathogens and activates B cells

F. A heating process that is used to kill microorganisms in food

G. An organism that causes disease

H. A white blood cell that engulfs pathogens in the inflammatory response

I. A disorder in which the immune system is overly sensitive to substances not normally found in the body

1. histamine
2. carcinogen
3. phagocyte
4. active immunity
5. antibiotic
6. immunity
7. pasteurization
8. T cell
9. antibody
10. pathogen
11. allergy
12. lymphocyte
13. vaccine

A ___	B ___	C ___	= _____
D ___	E ___	F ___	= _____
G ___	H ___	I ___	= _____
=	=	=	= _____
___	___	___	

= _____

© Prentice-Hall, Inc.

CHAPTER 15

THE NERVOUS SYSTEM

....

SECTION 15-1 **How the Nervous System Works**
(pages 486-490)

This section describes what the nervous system does in the body. It also tells how nerve impulses travel.

▶ Functions of the Nervous System (page 487)

1. List three functions of the nervous system.

    a. _____

    b. _____

    c. _____

2. Is the following sentence true or false? You can move without your

    nervous system. _____

3. From what two places does the nervous system receive information?

    a. _____   b. _____

4. Circle the letter of a change in the environment that can make an
   organism react.

    a. response   **b.** stimulus   **c.** homeostasis   **d.** nerve impulse

5. Is the following true or false? All nervous system responses are voluntary,

    or under your control. _____

6. How does the nervous system help maintain homeostasis? _____

    _____

    _____

© Prentice-Hall, Inc.

CHAPTER 15, The Nervous System *(continued)*

▶ The Neuron—A Message-Carrying Cell (pages 487–489)

Match each term with its definition.

Terms	Definitions
_____ 7. axon	**a.** The message that a nerve cell carries
_____ 8. dendrite	**b.** An extension from a nerve cell that carries impulses toward the nerve cell
_____ 9. neuron	**c.** An extension from a nerve cell that carries impulses away from the nerve cell
_____ 10. nerve impulse	**d.** A cell that carries information through the nervous system

11. Is the following sentence true or false? A neuron can have only one

    axon. _____

12. A bundle of nerve fibers is called a(n) _____.

13. Complete the flowchart to show the path of a nerve impulse.

Path of a Nerve Impulse

The telephone rings. Nerve impulses begin when a(n) _____ in the ear picks up the stimulus of the telephone ringing.

↓

The nerve impulse moves to _____ in the brain. The _____ interprets the impulses and decides to answer the phone.

↓

Nerve impulses from the brain move to _____. The muscles contract in response, and you pick up the telephone.

▶ How a Nerve Impulse Travels (page 490)

14. The tiny space between each axon tip and the next dendrite or muscle

    is called a(n) _____.

© Prentice-Hall, Inc.

15. How does a nerve impulse cross the gap between the axon and the next

structure? _____

_____

. . . .

SECTION 15–2 **Divisions of the Nervous System**
(pages 492–498)

This section explains the two major parts of the nervous system. It also describes what a reflex is.

▶ **Introduction** (page 492)

1. Complete the concept map to show the divisions of the nervous system.

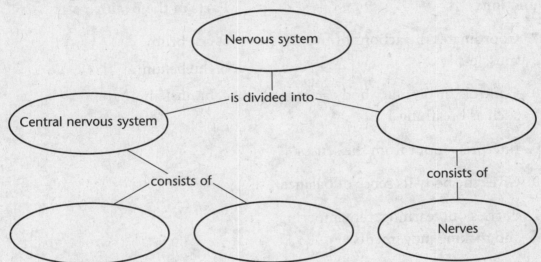

▶ **Central Nervous System Functions** (page 493)

2. Is the following sentence true or false? The central nervous system is

the control center of the body. _____

3. The part of the central nervous system that controls most functions in

the body is the _____.

4. The thick column of nerve tissue that links the brain to most of the

nerves is the _____.

© Prentice-Hall, Inc.

CHAPTER 15, The Nervous System *(continued)*

▶ Structure and Functions of the Brain (pages 493–495)

5. Is the following sentence true or false? Neurons in the brain are only

   interneurons. _____

6. What helps protect the brain from injury?

   a. _____

   b. _____

   c. _____

Match the parts of the brain with their functions. Each part of the brain
may be used more than once.

Functions	Parts of the Brain
_____ 7. Coordinates the actions of the muscles	**a.** cerebrum
_____ 8. Controls involuntary body actions, such as breathing	**b.** cerebellum
_____ 9. Interprets input from the senses	**c.** brainstem
_____ 10. Gives the body its sense of balance	
_____ 11. Carries out learning, remembering, and making judgements	

12. Is the following sentence true or false? The right half of the cerebrum

    controls the right side of the body. _____

13. Creativity and artistic ability are usually associated with the

    _____ side of the cerebrum.

▶ The Spinal Cord (page 495)

14. The spinal cord is the link between the _____ and the

    _____ .

© Prentice-Hall, Inc.

15. What protects the spinal cord?

a. _____

b. _____

c. _____

▶ Function of the Peripheral Nervous System (page 496)

16. What does the peripheral nervous system consist of? _____

_____

_____

_____

17. What is the function of the two groups of nerves making up the peripheral nervous system?

Somatic nervous system: _____

Autonomic nervous system: _____

▶ Reflexes (pages 497–498)

18. What is a reflex? _____

_____

_____

19. Circle the letter of each sentence that is true about reflexes.

a. In some reflex actions, the spinal cord, rather than the brain, directs the muscles to contract.

b. Reflexes protect you from getting hurt badly.

c. Nerve impulses move to the brain sooner than they do to the spinal cord.

d. The reflex action takes longer than it does for you to feel pain.

▶ Safety and the Nervous System (page 498)

20. A bruiselike injury of the brain is called a(n) _____ .

© Prentice-Hall, Inc.

CHAPTER 15, The Nervous System (continued)

21. What can decrease your chances of getting a brain injury? _____

_____

_____

22. What happens when the spinal cord is cut or crushed? _____

_____

_____

_____

• •

SECTION 15–3 ## The Senses (pages 500–507)

This section describes the senses and how they work to tell you about your environment.

▶ Introduction (page 500)

1. What are the major senses? _____

_____

2. The sense organs change information about the environment into

_____ and send them to the brain.

▶ Vision (pages 501–502)

Match the parts of the eye with their function.

Parts	Functions
_____ **3.** iris	**a.** The layer of receptor cells that lines the back of the eye where nerve impulses begin
_____ **4.** lens	**b.** Regulates the amount of light entering the eye and gives the eye its color
_____ **5.** cornea	**c.** The opening through which light enters the eye
_____ **6.** pupil	**d.** The clear tissue that covers the front of the eye
_____ **7.** retina	**e.** Focuses light

© Prentice-Hall, Inc.

8. Is the following sentence true or false? Cone cells work best in dim light and enable you to see black, white, and shades of gray.

_____

9. What two things happen to the image in the cerebrum?

a. _____

b. _____

▶ Correcting Vision Problems (pages 502–503)

10. Complete the table to show the two kinds of vision problems.

Vision Problems		
Questions	**Nearsightedness**	**Farsightedness**
What is wrong?		
What causes it?		
How is it corrected?		

▶ Hearing (pages 504–505)

11. Ears convert _____, a stimulus, to nerve impulses that your brain interprets.

12. How are sounds made? _____

_____

13. Is the following sentence true or false? Sound waves can travel only

through air. _____

14. The outer ear is shaped like a(n) _____ to gather sound waves.

15. Circle the letter of the membrane that vibrates when sound waves strike it.

a. outer ear   b. hammer   c. anvil   d. eardrum

16. What is the cochlea? _____

_____

© Prentice-Hall, Inc.

CHAPTER 15, The Nervous System *(continued)*

▶ Internal Stimuli and Balance (pages 505–506)

17. The structures in the ear that control your sense of balance are the

    _____.

18. Is the following sentence true or false? The cerebellum analyzes the

    impulses to determine if you are losing your balance. _____

▶ Smell and Taste (pages 506–507)

19. Is the following sentence true or false? The flavor of food is determined

    only by taste. _____

▶ Touch (page 507)

20. The largest sense organ is the _____.

21. Why is pain an important feeling? _____

    _____

 Reading Skill Practice

Photographs and illustrations in textbooks can help you understand what you have read. Look carefully at Figure 14 on page 502. What idea does this photograph communicate? Do your work on a separate sheet of paper.

SECTION 15–4 **Alcohol and Other Drugs**
(pages 508–516)

This section explains how drug abuse can affect the nervous system. It also describes how alcohol harms the body.

▶ Introduction (page 508)

1. Any chemical that causes changes in a person's body or behavior is a(n)

    _____.

© Prentice-Hall, Inc.

▶ Medicines (page 508)

2. What are medicines? _____

_____

_____

3. Is the following sentence true or false? It is not necessary to follow the

directions when taking medicines. _____

▶ Drug Abuse (pages 509–510)

4. The deliberate misuse of drugs for purposes other than medical ones is

called _____.

5. Circle the letter of each sentence that is true about drug abuse.

a. Medicines can never be abused.

b. Many abused drugs are illegal.

c. The use of illegal drugs is not dangerous to the body.

d. Abused drugs affect the body very shortly after they are taken.

6. The state in which a drug user needs larger and larger amounts of drugs

to produce the same effect on the body is called _____.

7. Circle the letter of the period of adjustment that occurs when a person
stops taking a drug.

a. addiction　　　**b.** tolerance　　　**c.** withdrawal　　　**d.** depressant

8. Is the following sentence true or false? When a person is emotionally
dependent on a drug, the person is used to the feelings and moods

produced by the drug. _____

▶ Other Effects of Drug Abuse (page 510)

9. What legal and social effects do drug abuse have? _____

_____

_____

© Prentice-Hall, Inc.

CHAPTER 15, The Nervous System *(continued)*

10. Is the following sentence true or false? If a person uses needles to inject a drug, that person has a chance of being infected with HIV.

    _____

▶ **Kinds of Drugs** (pages 510–513)

Match the kind of drug with its characteristics.

Kinds of Drug	Characteristics
_____ 11. depressant	a. Produces mood-altering effects when breathed in
_____ 12. stimulant	b. Synthetic chemical similar to hormones used by athletes to improve performance
_____ 13. inhalant	c. Slows down the activity of the central nervous system
_____ 14. hallucinogen	d. Can make people see or hear things that do not exist
_____ 15. anabolic steroid	e. Speeds up body processes

16. Look at Figure 22 on page 511. Which drugs do NOT cause emotional

    dependence? _____

    _____

▶ **Alcohol** (pages 513–516)

17. Circle the letter of the kind of drug that alcohol is.

    a. stimulant   **b.** depressant   **c.** anabolic steroid   **d.** inhalant

18. Is the following sentence true or false? Alcohol is the most commonly

    abused drug in people aged 12 to 17. _____

19. Alcohol is quickly absorbed by the _____ system.

20. Is the following sentence true or false? If alcohol is drunk with a meal, it

    takes longer for the alcohol to get into the blood. _____

© Prentice-Hall, Inc.

21. Complete the table to show the effects of alcohol on the body.

The Effects of Alcohol	
Body System	**Effects**
Nervous System	
Cardiovascular System	
Excretory System	

22. How does the abuse of alcohol affect the body? _____

_____

_____

_____

23. A disease in which a person is both physically addicted to and

emotionally dependent on alcohol is called _____.

24. Is the following sentence true or false? Alcoholics must go through

withdrawal to give up alcohol. _____

▶ Avoiding Drugs and Alcohol (page 516)

25. What is the best way to avoid depending on drugs and alcohol?

_____

_____

26. Many teenagers begin using drugs and alcohol because of

_____ from people who are abusing drugs.

© Prentice-Hall, Inc.

CHAPTER 15, The Nervous System (continued)

WordWise

Solve the clues by filling in the blanks with key terms from Chapter 15. Then write the numbered letters in the correct order to find the hidden question. Write the answer to the question.

Clues   **Key Terms**

A period of adjustment that occurs when a person   __ __ __ __ __ __ __ __ __ __ __
stops taking a drug   1   2

Controls your body's actions that occur automatically   __ __ __ __ __ __ __ __ __
                                                             3

Carries impulses toward the cell body of a neuron   __ __ __ __ __ __ __ __ __
                                                                             4

The layer of receptor cells that lines the back of the eye   __ __ __ __ __ __
                                                                       5

Regulates the amount of light entering the eye   __ __ __ __
                                                           6

A drug that slows down the activity of the central   __ __ __ __ __ __ __ __ __ __
nervous system   7

Another name for a nerve cell   __ __ __ __ __ __
                                          8

The largest part of the brain   __ __ __ __ __ __ __ __
                                     9

Describes a person to whom nearby objects   __ __ __ __ __ __ __ __ __ __
look blurry   10

The opening through which light enters the eye   __ __ __ __ __
                                                           11

The tiny space between each axon tip and the next   __ __ __ __ __ __ __
structure   12

Carries impulses away from the cell body of a neuron   __ __ __ __
                                                        13

Hidden Question: __ __ __ __ __   __ __   __   __ __ __ __ __ __ ?
                      1 2 3 4   5 6   7   8 9 10 11 12 13

Answer: _____

_____

© Prentice-Hall, Inc.

CHAPTER 16

THE ENDOCRINE SYSTEM AND REPRODUCTION

SECTION 16-1 **The Endocrine System**
(pages 522-526)

This section explains how the endocrine system works to control activities in the body.

▶ **The Role of the Endocrine System** (page 522)

1. What does the endocrine system control? _____

_____

_____

2. The endocrine system is made up of _____, organs that
   produce chemicals.

3. Is the following sentence true or false? Endocrine glands release their

   chemical products through delivery tubes. _____

▶ **Hormones** (pages 523-524)

4. The chemical product of an endocrine gland is a(n) _____,
   or chemical messenger.

5. How do hormones affect the body? _____

_____

6. Circle the letter of each sentence that is true about hormones.

   a. Hormones can regulate only the tissues and organs near the glands
      that produce them.

   b. Nerve impulses from the brain can cause the release of hormones.

   c. Hormones cause a slower, but longer-lasting response.

   d. Any hormone can affect any organ in the body.

© Prentice-Hall, Inc.

CHAPTER 16, The Endocrine System and Reproduction (*continued*)

7. A hormone interacts only with certain _____,
   cells that recognize the hormone's chemical structure.

Match the endocrine gland with the function of the hormone it produces.
See *Exploring the Endocrine System* on pages 524–525.

Glands	Functions of the Hormones
_____ **8.** thyroid gland	**a.** Control the changes that take place in the body of a teenage boy
_____ **9.** adrenal glands	**b.** Trigger the body to respond to emergencies
_____ **10.** ovaries	**c.** Produces insulin and glucagon
_____ **11.** testes	**d.** Controls the release of energy from food molecules during respiration
_____ **12.** pancreas	**e.** Control the changes in a teenage girl's body

▶ The Hypothalamus (page 524)

13. Circle the letter of each sentence that is true about the hypothalamus.

    a. The hypothalamus links the nervous system and the excretory system.

    b. The hypothalamus is located on the kidneys.

    c. The hypothalamus sends nerve messages and produces hormones.

    d. The hypothalamus plays a major role in maintaining homeostasis.

▶ The Pituitary Gland (page 525)

14. What is the pituitary gland? _____

    _____

    _____

15. Is the following sentence true or false? The pituitary gland releases
    hormones in response to nerve impulses or hormone signals from the

    hypothalamus. _____

© Prentice-Hall, Inc.

▶ **Negative Feedback** (page 526)

16. How does negative feedback work to control the amount of a hormone

in the blood? _____

_____

_____

_____

17. Complete the cycle diagram to show how thyroxine, a hormone
produced by the thyroid gland, is regulated by negative feedback.

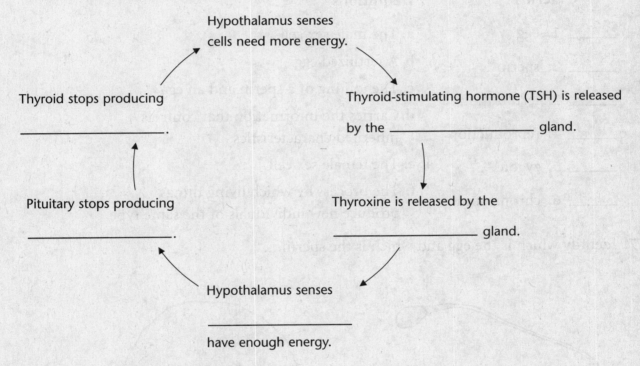

Hypothalamus senses
cells need more energy.

Thyroid stops producing
_____.

Thyroid-stimulating hormone (TSH) is released
by the _____ gland.

Thyroxine is released by the
_____ gland.

Pituitary stops producing
_____.

Hypothalamus senses

_____

have enough energy.

 Reading Skill Practice

Knowing the meanings of the key terms in a section will help you to better understand what you
are reading. Make a list of key terms in this section. Write the meanings of these terms using
your own words. In this way, the key terms become a natural part of your vocabulary. Do your
work on a separate sheet of paper.

© Prentice-Hall, Inc.

CHAPTER 16, The Endocrine System and Reproduction *(continued)*

● ●

SECTION 16–2 **The Male and Female Reproductive Systems**
(pages 527–532)

This section describes the structures and functions of the organs in the male and female reproductive systems. It also explains the events in the menstrual cycle.

▶ **Sex Cells** (pages 527–528)

Match each key term with its definition.

Terms	Definitions
_____ 1. egg	**a.** The male sex cell
_____ 2. sperm	**b.** A fertilized egg
_____ 3. fertilization	**c.** The joining of a sperm and an egg
_____ 4. reproduction	**d.** Carries the information that controls inherited characteristics
_____ 5. zygote	**e.** The female sex cell
_____ 6. chromosome	**f.** The process by which living things produce new individuals of the same type

7. Identify which is the egg and which is the sperm.

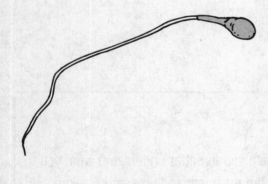

a. _____   **b.** _____

8. Is the following sentence true or false? A sex cell has the same number of

chromosomes as a body cell. _____

© Prentice-Hall, Inc.

▶ The Male Reproductive System (pages 528–529)

9. What is the male reproductive system specialized to produce?

    a. _____   **b.** _____

10. Circle the letter of the organs in the male where sperm are produced.

    a. testosterone   **b.** testes   **c.** scrotum   **d.** penis

11. What does testosterone control? _____

_____

12. The testes are located in an external pouch of skin called the

_____.

13. Is the following sentence true or false? Sperm can develop normally only in slightly cooler temperatures than normal body temperature.

_____

14. What does semen provide to sperm?

    a. _____

    b. _____

15. Semen leaves the body through an organ called the _____.

▶ The Female Reproductive System (pages 530–531)

16. What is the role of the female reproductive system? _____

_____

_____

17. What do ovaries produce?

    a. _____

    b. _____

18. What does estrogen control? _____

_____

_____

© Prentice-Hall, Inc.

CHAPTER 16, The Endocrine System and Reproduction *(continued)*

19. Complete the flowchart to show the path of an egg cell.

Path of an Egg

A(n) _____ produces an egg cell.

↓

The egg cell moves through the _____ where it can be fertilized.

↓

The egg enters the _____ where it stays to develop if it's fertilized.

↓

An unfertilized egg begins to break down and enters the muscular passageway

leading to the outside of the body called the _____, or birth canal.

▶ The Menstrual Cycle (pages 531–532)

20. Circle the letter of how often an egg is released from the ovaries.

    a. daily   **b.** weekly   **c.** monthly   **d.** yearly

21. The monthly cycle of changes that occurs in the female reproductive

system is called the _____.

22. What occurs during the menstrual cycle? _____

_____

_____

23. The menstrual cycle prepares the body for _____, the
condition that begins after fertilization has taken place.

24. Circle the letter of each sentence that is true about menstruation.

    a. Menstruation lasts about 28 days.

    b. Hormones of the endocrine system control the menstrual cycle.

    c. All girls begin menstruation at the same age.

    d. Women stop releasing eggs from their ovaries at about the age of 50.

© Prentice-Hall, Inc.

SECTION 16-3 The Human Life Cycle
(pages 533-541)

This section explains how babies develop before birth, what happens during birth, and what happens as babies develop into children. It also describes the changes that occur during adolescence.

▶ Introduction (page 533)

1. After fertilization, the zygote develops first into an embryo and then

   into a(n) _____.

▶ The Zygote (page 533)

2. Is the following sentence true or false? The zygote begins to divide to make two, and then four cells before it enters the uterus.

   _____

3. The growing mass of cells forms a hollow ball and attaches to the lining of the uterus, at which time the developing human is called a(n)

   _____.

▶ The Development of the Embryo (page 534)

4. The membrane that surrounds the embryo and develops into a fluid-

   filled sac is called the _____.

5. What is the placenta? _____

   _____

   _____

6. What is the function of the umbilical cord? _____

   _____

   _____

   _____

© Prentice-Hall, Inc.

CHAPTER 16, The Endocrine System and Reproduction (continued)

7. Is the following sentence true or false? Substances, such as chemicals from tobacco smoke and alcohol, can pass from the mother to the

   embryo. _____

▶ The Development of the Fetus (page 535)

8. Complete the table to show the development of the fetus.

The Development of the Fetus	
Time in Development	**What Is Happening**
Nine weeks	
From fourth to sixth month	
Final three months	

▶ Birth (pages 535–536)

9. List the three stages of the birth of a baby.

   a. _____   b. _____   c. _____

10. Circle the letter of each sentence that is true about birth.

    a. Strong muscular contractions, called labor, enlarge the cervix so that the baby fits through it.

    b. During delivery, the baby is pushed feet first out of the uterus, through the vagina, and out of the mother's body.

    c. After delivery, the umbilical cord is clamped and cut.

    d. After labor, contractions push out the placenta and other membranes into the vagina.

© Prentice-Hall, Inc.

11. How does the baby's body adjust to the stress of the birth process?

_____

_____

_____

▶ Multiple Births (page 537)

12. What is a multiple birth? _____

_____

_____

Match the type of twins with its characteristics. Each type of twins may be used more than once.

Characteristics	Types of Twins
_____ **13.** Develop from a single fertilized egg	**a.** identical twins
_____ **14.** Develop when two eggs are released from the ovary and fertilized by two different sperm	**b.** fraternal twins
_____ **15.** Are no more alike than any brothers or sisters	
_____ **16.** Have identical inherited traits and are the same sex	

▶ Infancy (pages 537–538)

17. Is the following sentence true or false? As a baby grows, its head grows more slowly, and its body, legs, and arms grow quickly to catch up.

_____

18. Circle the letter of the physical skill that babies develop first.

    a. crawl   **b.** grasp objects   **c.** walk   **d.** hold up their heads

19. Is the following sentence true or false? Babies can communicate only by

crying. _____

© Prentice-Hall, Inc.

CHAPTER 16, The Endocrine System and Reproduction (continued)

▶ Childhood (page 538)

20. Circle the letter of each sentence that is true about childhood.

    a. Childhood begins at about the age of 13 years.

    b. Children become taller and heavier and become more coordinated.

    c. As they develop, children become less curious.

    d. Children learn to think about and care for others as they grow.

21. What does an increased appetite toward the end of childhood signal?

    _____

    _____

▶ Adolescence (pages 539–540)

22. What is adolescence? _____

    _____

    _____

23. The physical changes that occur during adolescence are controlled by

    _____ produced by the endocrine system.

24. What is puberty? _____

    _____

25. Circle the letter of each physical change of puberty that occurs in girls.

    a. voice deepens   b. ovulation starts
    c. body odor increases   d. hips widen

26. Circle the letter of each physical change of puberty that occurs in boys.

    a. hips widen   b. sperm are produced
    c. hair grows on face   d. body odor increases

27. During adolescence, _____ tend to have their growth

    spurt at a younger age than _____ do.

© Prentice-Hall, Inc.

28. Is the following sentence true or false? All adolescents grow and develop

at the same rate. _____

29. Is the following sentence true or false? Adolescence includes only the

physical changes of puberty. _____

30. Circle the letter of each sentence that is true about changes in the way
teenagers feel.

　a. Teenagers always have the same feelings about the changes they are
　　experiencing.

　b. Teenagers can think about the consequences of their actions.

　c. During adolescence, memory and problem-solving skills improve.

　d. Teens are not able to develop mental abilities through their interests
　　outside of school.

31. What is peer pressure? _____

_____

32. Peer pressure that is _____ can lead teens to do things
that go against their values.

▶ Life as an Adult (page 541)

33. Is the following sentence true or false? Adulthood definitely begins at

the age of 18 years. _____

34. Circle the letter of the age when the process of aging begins.

　a. 20 years　　　**b.** 30 years　　　**c.** 40 years　　　**d.** 50 years

35. What changes occur to the body during aging? _____

_____

_____

_____

36. Is the following sentence true or false? The effects of aging can be
slowed if people follow sensible diets and exercise regularly.

_____

© Prentice-Hall, Inc.

CHAPTER 16, The Endocrine System and Reproduction *(continued)*

....

**SECTION
16–4** **Reproduction and Genetics**
(pages 543-547)

This section describes how genes are passed from one generation to the next through sexual reproduction and asexual reproduction. It also describes what causes different traits.

▶ Introduction (page 543)

1. The process in which characteristics pass from parents to offspring is

   called _____.

2. The scientific study of heredity is called _____.

▶ DNA and Genes (page 544)

3. The shape of a person's nose and the length of a kitten's hair are

   examples of _____.

4. What is a gene? _____

   _____

   _____

▶ Sexual Reproduction (pages 544–545)

5. Is the following sentence true or false? Sexual reproduction is the kind of
   reproduction that involves two parents who combine their genetic

   material to produce a new organism. _____

▶ Asexual Reproduction (page 545)

6. A bacterium dividing in two and a hydra budding are examples of

   _____.

© Prentice-Hall, Inc.

7. Complete the table to show the differences between sexual reproduction and asexual reproduction.

Two Kinds of Reproduction		
Type of Reproduction	Number of Parents	Similarity of Offspring
Sexual		
Asexual		

▶ Alleles (page 546)

8. What are alleles? _____

_____

▶ Dominant and Recessive (pages 546–547)

9. Is the following sentence true or false? If an individual has one dominant allele and one recessive allele, the trait that is caused by the

recessive allele will show up. _____

10. In pea plants, what are the two alleles for color?

   a.   b.

11. The purple allele is dominant. What alleles must a pea plant have in

order to have white flowers? _____

12. What alleles must a pea plant have in order to have purple flowers?

_____

_____

_____

13. Is the following sentence true or false? The inherited characteristics of any organism are controlled by the alleles that make up its genes.

_____

© Prentice-Hall, Inc.

CHAPTER 16, The Endocrine System and Reproduction (continued)

WordWise

Use the clues to identify key terms from Chapter 16. Write the terms on the lines. Then find the words hidden in the puzzle and circle them. Words are across or up-and-down.

Clues	Key Terms
The chemical product of an endocrine gland	_____
The stage of development in which the developing human attaches to the lining of the uterus	_____
The stage of development from the ninth week of development until birth	_____
The period of sexual development in which the body becomes able to reproduce	_____
A fertilized egg	_____
The mixture of sperm cells and fluids	_____
The female organ that produces egg cells and hormones like estrogen	_____
The hormone in females that triggers the development of some adult female characteristics	_____
A physical characteristic of an organism	_____
Different forms of a gene	_____

```
p  g  e  s  t  r  o  g  e  n  m  z
u  o  t  s  e  m  e  n  p  j  t  y
b  v  h  d  e  u  a  i  s  z  r  g
e  a  f  e  t  u  s  p  h  u  a  o
r  r  i  o  e  m  b  r  y  o  i  t
t  y  a  l  l  e  l  e  s  o  t  e
y  c  p  h  o  r  m  o  n  e  w  t
```

© Prentice-Hall, Inc.

CHAPTER 17

ECOSYSTEMS AND BIOMES

....

SECTION 17–1 **Energy Flow in Ecosystems** (pages 558–565)

This section explains the different roles that organisms play in the movement of energy through an ecosystem. The section also describes how organisms in the different roles interact to form food chains and food webs.

▶ What are the Components of an Ecosystem? (pages 558–559)

1. The components of an ecosystem are all the _____ and

   _____ things that interact in a particular area.

2. Is the following sentence true or false? The organisms in an ecosystem

   are called abiotic factors. _____

3. Sunlight and temperature are examples of _____ in an

   ecosystem.

▶ Habitat and Niche (page 559)

Match the element of an ecosystem with its definition.

_____ **4.** habitat

_____ **5.** species

_____ **6.** niche

a. A group of similar organisms that can mate with one another an produce fertile offspring

b. An organism's role in an ecosystem

c. The specific environment that provides the things an organism needs

7. The food a bird eats and the organisms that feed on the bird are parts of

   the bird's _____ .

© Prentice-Hall, Inc.

CHAPTER 17, Ecosystems and Biomes (continued)

▶ Energy Roles (pages 560–562)

Match the energy role with its definition.

Energy Role	Definition
_____ 8. producer	a. Organism that breaks down wastes and dead organisms
_____ 9. consumer	b. Organism that obtains energy by feeding on other organisms
_____ 10. decomposer	c. Organism that can make its own food

11. What types of organisms are producers? _____

_____

_____

12. Is the following sentence true or false? Energy enters all ecosystems as

sunlight. _____

13. Is the following sentence true or false? Producers are the source of all

the food in an ecosystem. _____

14. List two major groups of decomposers.

a. _____   b. _____

15. Complete the compare/contrast table.

Types of Consumers	
Type of Consumer	**Type of Food**
	Only plants
Carnivore	
	Both plants and animals
	Dead organisms

© Prentice-Hall, Inc.

16. Is the following sentence true or false? Decomposers return raw

materials to the environment. _____

▶ Food Chains and Food Webs (pages 562–564)

17. What is a food chain? _____

_____

_____

18. Label the producer and the first-level and second-level consumers in
the food chain.

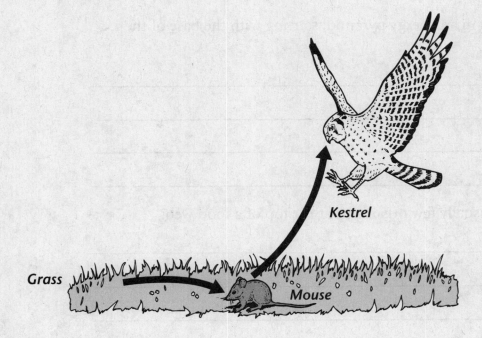

Kestrel

Grass

Mouse

19. The many overlapping food chains in an ecosystem make up a(n)

_____.

20. Circle the letter of each sentence that is true about a food web.

a. Producers are at the top of the food web.

b. All first-level consumers are carnivores.

c. Second-level consumers may be carnivores or omnivores.

d. An organism may play more than one role in a food web.

© Prentice-Hall, Inc.

CHAPTER 17, Ecosystems and Biomes *(continued)*

▶ Energy Pyramids (pages 564–565)

21. What does an energy pyramid show? _____

_____

22. Circle the letter of each sentence that is true about an energy pyramid.

    a. The greatest amount of energy is available at the producer level.

    b. At each level of the pyramid, there is more energy available.

    c. About half the energy at one level is transferred to the next.

    d. Most food webs have only three or four feeding levels.

23. Name the levels in an energy pyramid, starting with the base of the pyramid.

    a. _____

    b. _____

    c. _____

    d. _____

24. Why are there usually few organisms at the top of a food web?

_____

_____

_____

 Reading Skill Practice

Outlining is a way to help yourself understand and remember what you have read. Write an outline of this section on energy flow in ecosystems. In an outline, copy the headings in the textbook. Under each heading, write the main idea of that part of the lesson. Then list the details that support each main idea.

© Prentice-Hall, Inc.

SECTION 17–3 Biogeography (pages 566-567)

This section describes why organisms are found where they are and how organisms can move from one place to another. The section also describes factors that limit the movement of organisms from place to place.

▶ Introduction (page 566)

1. The study of where organisms live is called _____.

▶ Continental Drift (pages 566–567)

2. What is continental drift? _____

_____

3. Is the following sentence true or false? Scientists hypothesize that the movement of the continents has had little impact on the distribution of species. _____

▶ Means of Dispersal (pages 567–568)

4. The movement of organisms from one place to another is called

_____.

5. Complete the concept map.

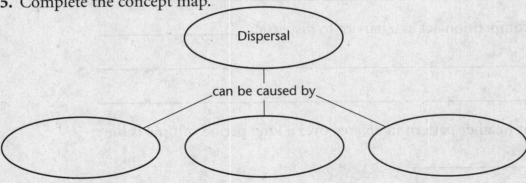

6. What organisms are dispersed by the wind? _____

_____

_____

© Prentice-Hall, Inc.

CHAPTER 17, Ecosystems and Biomes *(continued)*

7. Give examples of ways organisms may be dispersed by other living things.

_____

_____

_____

_____

8. Is the following sentence true or false? Humans are not important to

the dispersal of other species. _____

9. Species that have naturally evolved in an area are called

_____. Species that have been carried into a

new locale by people are called _____.

▶ Limits to Dispersal (pages 568–569)

10. List three factors that limit dispersal of a species.

a. _____ b. _____ c. _____

11. What are some examples of physical barriers that limit dispersal?

_____

_____

12. How can competition act as a barrier to dispersal? _____

_____

_____

13. The typical weather pattern in an area over a long period of time is the

area's _____.

14. Is the following sentence true or false? Places with similar climates tend

to have species that occupy similar niches. _____

© Prentice-Hall, Inc.

SECTION 17-3 Earth's Biomes (pages 572-583)

This section describes several different biomes, or groups of similar ecosystems, that are found on planet Earth. The section also tells where the different biomes are located.

▶ Introduction (page 572)

1. A group of ecosystems with similar climates and organisms is called

   a(n) _____.

2. Is the following sentence true or false? Different environments support

   different types of organisms. _____

▶ Rain Forest Biomes (pages 573–574)

3. Circle the letter of each sentence that is true about tropical rain forests.

   a. They are found only in Africa and South America.

   b. They receive a lot of rainfall and sunlight year-round.

   c. They contain a limited number of species.

   d. They are much warmer in some seasons than in others.

4. The tall trees in a tropical rain forest form a leafy roof called the

   _____.

5. Where are temperate rain forests located? _____

   _____

▶ Desert Biomes (pages 574–575)

6. Circle the letter of each sentence that is true about deserts.

   a. They receive less than 10 centimeters of rain per year.

   b. They have more evaporation than precipitation.

   c. They are always hot.

   d. They have extreme temperatures.

© Prentice-Hall, Inc.

CHAPTER 17, Ecosystems and Biomes *(continued)*

▶ Grassland Biomes (pages 575–576)

7. Circle the letter of each sentence that is true about grasslands.

   a. They have many trees.

   b. They have rich soil.

   c. They receive more than 75 centimeters of rain each year.

   d. They are home to many of the largest animals on Earth.

8. Grasslands that are located closer to the equator than prairies are called

   _____.

▶ Deciduous Forest Biomes (pages 576–577)

9. Trees that shed their leaves and grow new ones each year are called

   _____.

10. Circle the letter of the sentence that is true about deciduous forests.

    a. They receive at least 50 centimeters of rain each year.

    b. Their temperatures are constant throughout the year.

    c. Their growing season usually lasts for 10 months.

    d. They contain very few habitats.

▶ Boreal Forest Biomes (pages 577–578)

11. What type of trees are found in a boreal forest? _____

    _____

12. Circle the letter of each sentence that is true about boreal forests.

    a. They are farther north than deciduous forests.

    b. They have very cold winters.

    c. They receive little snow.

    d. Their most common species of trees are fir, spruce, and hemlock.

▶ Tundra Biomes (pages 578–579)

13. An extremely cold, dry, land biome is the _____.

© Prentice-Hall, Inc.

14. Plants in the tundra include _____ forms of trees.

▶ Mountains and Ice (page 579)

15. Is the following sentence true or false? If you hiked to the top of a tall

mountain, you would pass through a series of biomes. _____

16. What are some organisms adapted to life on the ice? _____

_____

▶ Freshwater Biomes (pages 580–581)

17. Circle the letter of each sentence that is true about water biomes.
    a. They cover about one quarter of Earth's surface.
    b. They include both freshwater and saltwater biomes.
    c. They are affected by temperature, sunlight, oxygen, and salt content.
    d. Their most common producers are plants.

18. Is the following sentence true or false? Lakes are generally larger and

deeper than ponds. _____

19. Streams and rivers are examples of _____ water.

▶ Marine Biomes (pages 581–583)

20. Complete the compare/contrast table.

Types of Marine Biomes	
Type of Biome	**Where It Is Located**
Estuary	Where fresh river water and salty ocean water meet
	Between the highest and lowest tide
	Below the low-tide line and out over the continental shelf
	On the surface of the open ocean
	Below the surface of the open ocean

© Prentice-Hall, Inc.

CHAPTER 17, Ecosystems and Biomes (continued)

21. Is the following sentence true or false? An estuary is a very poor habitat

for living things. _____

22. Why is the intertidal zone a difficult place to live? _____

_____

_____

23. Circle the letter of each sentence that is true about the neritic zone.

   a. Its water is too deep for photosynthesis to occur.

   b. It is particularly rich in living things.

   c. Many large schools of fish feed there.

   d. Coral reefs may form there.

24. Is the following sentence true or false? Algae form the basis of almost

all open-ocean food webs. _____

SECTION 17-4 Succession: Equilibrium in Ecosystems (pages 586-588)

This section describes a series of predictable changes that occur in a community over time.

▶ Introduction (page 586)

1. What is ecological succession? _____

_____

2. A community in an ecosystem is in _____ when the

numbers and species of organisms in it do not change suddenly.

▶ Primary Succession (page 587)

3. What is primary succession? _____

_____

_____

© Prentice-Hall, Inc.

4. Circle the letter of each choice that describes an area where primary succession might occur.

   a. A new island formed by the eruption of an undersea volcano

   b. An area of bare rock uncovered by a melting ice sheet

   c. A clearing in a forest left by cutting down the trees

   d. An area without any trees or other plants following a forest fire

5. The first species to populate the area in primary succession are called

   _____.

6. Pioneer species are often _____ and _____.

7. Is the following sentence true or false? Primary succession may lead to a

   community of organisms in equilibrium, which does not change

   drastically unless the ecosystem is disturbed. _____

▶ **Secondary Succession** (page 588)

8. The series of changes that occur after a disturbance in an existing

   ecosystem is called _____.

9. What natural disturbances can result in secondary succession? _____

   _____

   _____

10. What human activities can result in secondary succession? _____

    _____

    _____

11. Is the following sentence true or false? Secondary succession occurs

    more slowly than primary succession. _____

12. Secondary succession restores the ecosystem to a state in which

    _____ can be maintained.

© Prentice-Hall, Inc.

CHAPTER 17, Ecosystems and Biomes *(continued)*

WordWise

Match each definition in the left column with the correct term in the right column. Then write the number of each term in the appropriate box below. When you have filled all the boxes, add up the numbers in each column, row, and two diagonals. All the sums should be the same.

Definitions

A. Consumer that eats both plants and animals

B. Carnivore that feeds on the bodies of dead organisms

C. A state of balance in an ecosystem

D. An area that receives less than 25 centimeters of rain a year

E. Movement of organisms from one place to another

F. Average conditions of temperature, precipitation, winds, and clouds in an area

G. Group of ecosystems with similar climates and organisms

H. Permanently frozen soil found in the tundra climate region

I. Series of predictable changes that occur in a community over time

Terms

1. scavenger

2. biome

3. climate

4. succession

5. dispersal

6. omnivore

7. desert

8. equilibrium

9. permafrost

A ____	B ____	C ____	= ____
D ____	E ____	F ____	= ____
G ____	H ____	I ____	= ____
= ____	= ____	= ____	= ____

© Prentice-Hall, Inc.

CHAPTER 18

RELATING TO THE ENVIRONMENT

SECTION 18–1 **Adaptations and the Environment** (pages 594-599)

This section describes examples of adaptations. It also explains the importance of adaptations for survival.

▶ Adaptations (pages 594–595)

1. What is an adaptation? _____

_____

_____

2. Complete the concept map to show a wolf's adaptations to get food.

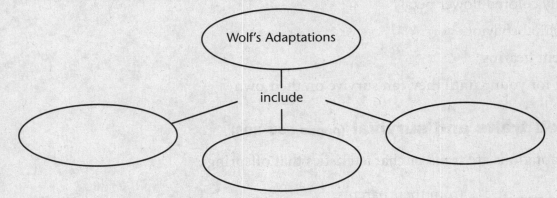

3. Is the following sentence true or false? A frog is a "sit and wait" predator.

_____

▶ Surviving in Different Environments (pages 595–597)

4. Is the following sentence true or false? Organisms need different

adaptations to survive in different environments. _____

© Prentice-Hall, Inc.

CHAPTER 18, Relating to the Environment *(continued)*

5. How are flowers of the pasque plant an adaptation that keeps the plant

warm? _____

_____

_____

6. Describe the woodpecker's adaptations for getting food. _____

_____

_____

▶ Reproductive Adaptations (page 598)

7. Is the following sentence true or false? Organisms have very few

adaptations that help ensure that reproduction will take place and

that new organisms will survive. _____

8. Circle the letter of each reproductive adaptation.

   a. brightly colored flower petals

   b. courtship behavior

   c. excellent hearing

   d. caring for young until they can survive on their own

▶ Inherited traits and survival (pages 598–599)

9. Most adaptations are traits or characteristics that offspring

   _____ from their parents.

10. Adaptations are determined by an organism's _____.

▶ Adaptation and Environmental Change (page 599)

11. What determines whether an organism can adapt to an environment

that has changed? _____

_____

© Prentice-Hall, Inc.

Science Explorer Grade 7

12. How does the ability to eat many different foods help an animal survive if one of its food sources disappears due to changes in the

environment? _____

_____

. . . .

SECTION 18-2 **Animal Behavior**
(pages 600-606)

This section describes how the behavior of an animal helps it to survive. It also explains the difference between learned behavior and instinct.

▶ Introduction (pages 600–601)

1. All of the actions that an animal performs, such as the things it does to get food, avoid predators, or find a mate are part of the animal's

_____.

▶ Behavior—An Important Adaptation (page 601)

2. In what two ways do most behaviors help an animal? _____

_____

3. An organism's reaction to a stimulus is a(n) _____.

▶ Instinctive Behavior (page 602)

4. A behavior pattern that is inborn and that an animal performs correctly

the first time is a(n) _____.

5. Circle the letter of each behavior that is an instinct.

a. A lion hunting its prey.   b. A spider spinning a web.

c. A bird building a nest.   d. Earthworms crawling away from
                                        bright light.

▶ Learning (pages 602–605)

6. What is learning? _____

_____

© Prentice-Hall, Inc.

CHAPTER 18, Relating to the Environment (continued)

7. Circle the letter of each sentence that is true about learning.

   a. The smaller an animal's brain is, the more the animal can learn.

   b. Learned behaviors are usually done perfectly the first time.

   c. All learned behaviors depend partly on inherited traits.

   d. Animals must practice in order to develop the abilities they have inherited.

8. Complete the concept map to show three different kinds of learning.

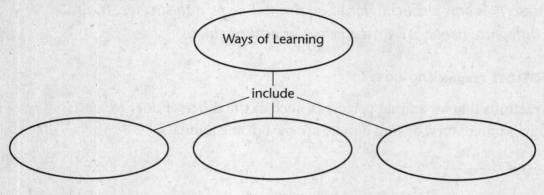

9. How did Pavlov condition a dog to salivate when he rang a bell?

   _____

10. Learning to ride a bike is an example of _____ learning.

11. Is the following sentence true or false? Insight learning is most common in certain animals, such as gorillas, chimpanzees, and

    humans. _____

12. The capacity of a computer to perform complex tasks such as learning

    from experience and solving problems is called _____

    _____ .

▶ Imprinting (pages 605–606)

13. Certain newly hatched birds and newborn mammals learn to recognize and follow the first moving object they see in a process called

    _____ .

© Prentice-Hall, Inc.

14. In what two ways is imprinting valuable?

a. _____

_____

b. _____

_____

15. Is the following sentence true or false? Once imprinting takes place, it

cannot be changed. _____

📖 Reading Skill Practice

The photographs and illustrations in a textbook can help you better understand what you are reading. Look at Figure 8 on page 605. What idea does this illustration communicate?

SECTION 18-3 ## Patterns of Behavior (pages 608-615)

This section tells about different behaviors that help animals survive.

▶ Competition and Aggression (page 609)

1. Circle the letter of each resource that animals compete for.

a. food   b. water   c. space   d. shelter

2. Threatening behavior that one animal uses to gain control over another

is called _____.

▶ Establishing a Territory (pages 609-610)

3. What is a territory? _____

_____

_____

© Prentice-Hall, Inc.

CHAPTER 18, Relating to the Environment *(continued)*

4. Circle the letter of each sentence that is true about establishing territories.

   a. An animal must compete with other animals for resources in its territory.

   b. A territory gives an animal unlimited access to food and possible mates.

   c. A territory provides a safe area in which animals can raise their young.

   d. A male songbird without a territory can easily attract a female.

▶ Mating and Raising Young (pages 610–611)

5. The behavior in which males and females of the same species prepare for

   mating is called _____.

6. What is the importance of courtship behavior? _____

   _____

   _____

7. Is the following sentence true or false? Most fishes, amphibians, and reptiles feed and protect their young, and teach them how to survive.

   _____

▶ Living in Groups (pages 611–612)

8. Look carefully at Figure 12 on page 611. Describe what the musk oxen

   are doing. _____

   _____

9. A group of closely related animals of the same species that work together

   for the benefit of the whole group is called a(n) _____.

▶ Communication (page 612)

10. List four ways in which animals communicate with each other.

    a. _____ **b.** _____

    c. _____ **d.** _____

© Prentice-Hall, Inc.

Match how an animal communicates with the information it is communicating.

Kind of information	Way of communicating
_____ 11. courtship	**a.** Growling and snarling animal
_____ 12. defense and aggression	**b.** Chirping male crickets
_____ 13. warnings	**c.** Dancing honeybee
_____ 14. food	**d.** Yipping prairie dog

▶ Behavior Cycles (pages 613–614)

15. Behavior cycles that take place over a period of about one day are called

_____.

16. How does hibernation help an animal survive? _____

_____

_____

17. Is the following sentence true or false? Animals that are active at night do not encounter predators that are active during the day.

_____

▶ Migration (pages 614–615)

18. The regular, periodic journey of an animal from one place to another

and then back again is called _____.

19. Why do animals migrate? _____

_____

_____

20. What senses do animals use to migrate? _____

_____

_____

© Prentice-Hall, Inc.

CHAPTER 18, Relating to the Environment (*continued*)

WordWise

Answer the clues to solve the crossword puzzle.

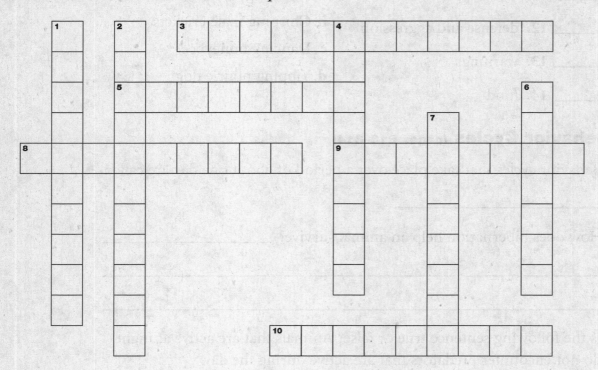

Clues down

1. Process in which newly hatched birds learn to recognize and follow the first moving object they see

2. State of greatly reduced body activity during the winter

4. Area that is occupied and defended by an animal or group of animals

6. Group of closely related animals of the same species that work together to benefit the whole group

7. An internal or external signal that causes a living thing to react in some way

Clues across

3. Learning to connect some kind of stimulus with a good or bad event

5. Term used to describe all the actions an animal performs

8. Regular, periodic journey of an animal from one place to another and then back again

9. Inborn behavior that is performed correctly the first time

10. Behavior in which males and females of the same species prepare for mating

© Prentice-Hall, Inc.

CHAPTER 19

LIVING RESOURCES

Environmental Issues
(pages 622-626)

This section describes three main types of environmental issues and three different approaches to resolving them. The section also describes how lawmakers weigh the costs and benefits of proposals to deal with environmental issues.

▶ Effects of Human Activity (pages 622–623)

1. Complete the concept map.

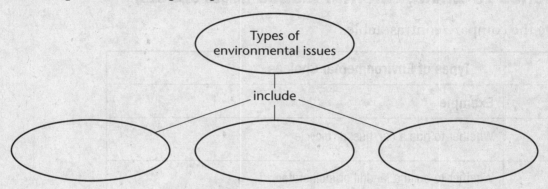

Match the term with its definition.

Term	Definition
_____ **2.** natural resource	**a.** Resources that are not replaced as they are used
_____ **3.** renewable resource	**b.** Resources that are naturally replaced in a relatively short time
_____ **4.** nonrenewable resource	**c.** Anything in the environment that is used by people

5. Circle the letter of the sentence that is true about the human population.

a. It grew rapidly until A.D. 1650. b. It grew slowly until A.D. 1950.

c. It was 6 billion by A.D. 2000. d. It was 1 billion in A.D. 1000.

© Prentice-Hall, Inc.

CHAPTER 19, Living Resources *(continued)*

6. Why did the human population grow so rapidly in recent centuries?

_____

_____

_____

7. Any change to the environment that has a negative effect on living

things is called _____.

8. What are some human activities that result in pollution? _____

_____

_____

▶ Approaches to Environmental Issues (pages 624–625)

9. Complete the compare/contrast table.

Types of Environmental Choices	
Choice	**Example**
	Whether to ride a car, bus, or bicycle
	Whether to build a landfill or incinerator
	Whether to allow drilling for oil in a wildlife refuge
	How to protect Earth's atmosphere

10. The study of the natural processes that occur in the environment and

how humans can affect them is called _____.

▶ Weighing Costs and Benefits (page 626)

11. Is the following sentence true or false? Costs and benefits are measured

only in terms of money. _____

© Prentice-Hall, Inc.

12. Circle the letter of each choice that would be a cost of drilling for oil in Antarctica.

   a. Transporting the oil

   b. Risk of oil spills

   c. Many new jobs

   d. Potential harm to sea animals

. . . .

SECTION 19-2 Forests and Fisheries (pages 628-632)

This section describes resources that come from forests and from areas of the ocean called fisheries. The section also explains how forests and fisheries are managed to protect them for future use.

▶ Forest Resources (page 628)

1. What are some valuable materials or products provided by forests?

   _____

   _____

   _____

2. Circle the letter of each sentence that is a reason people benefit from trees.

   a. Trees produce carbon dioxide.

   b. Trees absorb pollutants.

   c. Trees help prevent flooding.

   d. Trees help control soil erosion.

▶ Managing Forests (pages 629-630)

3. Is the following sentence true or false? Nearly a third of the area of the United States is covered with forests. _____

4. Is the following sentence true or false? Forests are a nonrenewable resource. _____

© Prentice-Hall, Inc.

CHAPTER 19, Living Resources (continued)

5. Complete the compare/contrast table.

Advantages and Disadvantages of Different Logging Methods		
Logging Method	**Advantages**	**Disadvantages**
	Quicker, cheaper, safer	Exposes soil to erosion
	Less damaging to habitat	Can be dangerous to loggers

6. A regular amount of a renewable resource that can be harvested without reducing the future supply is called a(n) _____.

7. How can forests provide a sustainable yield? _____

_____

_____

8. What is certified wood? _____

_____

_____

▶ Fisheries (pages 631–632)

9. An area with a large population of valuable ocean organisms is called

a(n) _____.

Match the approach to managing fisheries with its example.

Approach	**Example**
_____ **10.** fishing limits	**a.** Requiring the use of nets that allow young fish to escape
_____ **11.** fishing methods	**b.** Introducing unusual species of fish as food
_____ **12.** aquaculture	**c.** Setting an upper limit on the amount of fish that can be caught
_____ **13.** new resources	**d.** Raising fish in an artificial pond

© Prentice-Hall, Inc.

Reading Skill Practice

The illustrations in a textbook can help you better understand what you are reading. Look at figure 7 on page 630. What does this illustration compare and contrast?

· ·

SECTION 19–3 **Biodiversity** (pages 634–642)

This section describes factors that affect biodiversity. The section also explains why biodiversity is valuable, how it is being threatened, and what is being done to protect it.

▶ Introduction (page 634)

1. The number of different species in an area is called its _____.

▶ Factors Affecting Biodiversity (pages 634–635)

2. Complete the concept map.

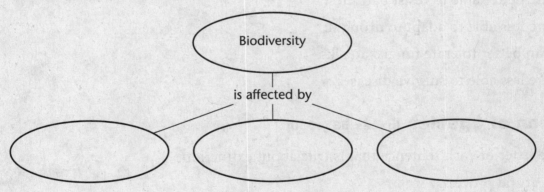

3. Circle the letter of each sentence that is true about biodiversity.

   a. Large areas contain more species than small areas.

   b. The number of species decreases from the poles toward the equator.

   c. Tropical rain forests are the most diverse ecosystems.

   d. Coral reefs are the second most diverse ecosystems.

© Prentice-Hall, Inc.

CHAPTER 19, Living Resources (continued)

▶ The Value of Biodiversity (pages 635–636)

4. Is the following sentence true or false? Biodiversity has no economic

    value. _____

5. A species that influences the survival of many other species in an

    ecosystem is called a(n) _____.

6. Is the following sentence true or false? If a keystone species disappears,

    the entire ecosystem may change. _____

▶ Gene Pool Diversity (page 637)

7. The individual differences in genes among members of a species make

    up the total _____ of that species.

8. Circle the letter of each sentence that is true about species with diverse
    gene pools.

    a. They are better able to resist parasites.

    b. They are less able to adapt to drought.

    c. They can better tolerate fungus attacks.

    d. They are less able to survive disease.

▶ Extinction of Species (pages 637–638)

9. Circle the letter of each sentence that is true about extinction.

    a. It is a natural process.

    b. Many species are now extinct.

    c. Extinctions have occurred only in the last few centuries.

    d. The number of species becoming extinct has increased dramatically.

10. Is the following sentence true or false? Once a population drops below a

    certain level, the species may not be able to recover. _____

11. A(n) _____ species is in danger of becoming extinct in
    the near future.

© Prentice-Hall, Inc.

▶ Causes of Extinction (pages 639–640)

12. What natural catastrophes might cause extinction? _____

_____

_____

13. Is the following sentence true or false? The major cause of extinction is

habitat fragmentation. _____

Match the term with its definition.

Term	Definition
_____ **14.** habitat destruction	**a.** Breaking larger habitats into smaller, isolated pieces
_____ **15.** habitat fragmentation	**b.** Illegally killing or removing wildlife species
_____ **16.** poaching	**c.** Loss of a natural habitat

17. How does introducing an exotic species affect an ecosystem? _____

_____

_____

18. How can pollutants affect organisms? _____

_____

_____

▶ Protecting Biodiversity (pages 641–642)

19. The mating of animals in zoos or wildlife preserves to protect severely

endangered species is called _____.

20. Is the following sentence true or false? Laws can help protect individual

species. _____

21. Is the following sentence true or false? The most effective way to preserve

biodiversity is to protect individual species. _____

© Prentice-Hall, Inc.

CHAPTER 19, Living Resources (continued)

WordWise

Review key terms from Chapter 19 by solving the crossword puzzle.

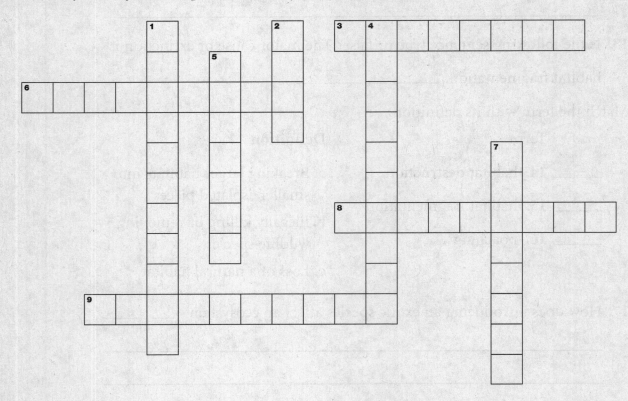

Clues down

1. Practice of raising fish and other water organisms for food
2. Structure in an organism's cells that carries its hereditary information
4. Term used to describe a species that is in danger of becoming extinct
5. Area with a large population of valuable ocean organisms
7. Hunting wildlife illegally

Clues across

3. Term used to describe a species that influences the survival of many others in an ecosystem
6. Change to the environment that has a negative effect on living things
8. Term used to describe resources that are replaced naturally
9. Term used to describe a species that could become endangered

© Prentice-Hall, Inc.